TYCHO BRAHE'S
DESCRIPTION OF HIS INSTRUMENTS
AND SCIENTIFIC WORK

DET KONGELIGE DANSKE VIDENSKABERNES SELSKAB

TYCHO BRAHE'S
DESCRIPTION OF HIS INSTRUMENTS
AND SCIENTIFIC WORK

AS GIVEN IN

ASTRONOMIAE INSTAURATAE MECHANICA
(WANDESBURGI 1598)

TRANSLATED AND EDITED BY

HANS RÆDER, ELIS STRÖMGREN
AND
BENGT STRÖMGREN

KØBENHAVN
I KOMMISSION HOS EJNAR MUNKSGAARD
1946

BRAHER   BILLER

RVDER   VLFSTANDER

LONGER   RØNNOR

ROSENKRANS   TROLLER

AXELLSØNNER   LONGER

MARCKEMAN   ROSENSPAR

KABBELER   STORMVASE

GVLDENSTERN   AXELLSØNNER

NON HABERI   SED ESSE

EFFIGIES TYCHONIS BRAHE OTTONIDIS DANI
DÑI DE KNVDSTRVP ET ARCIS VRANIENBVRG IN
INSVLA HELLISPONTI DANICI HVENNA FVNDATORIS
INSTRVMENTORVMQ´ ASTRONOMICORVM IN EADEM
DISPOSITARVM INVENTORIS ET STRVCTORIS
ÆTATIS SVÆ ANNO 40. ANNO DÑI. 1586. COMPL.

Dedicated to the Memory of
TYCHO BRAHE
on the occasion of the fourth centenary of his birth, 14th December 1946.

PRINTED IN DENMARK
BIANCO LUNOS BOGTRYKKERI

PREFACE

In 1598 Tycho Brahe published his Astronomiae Instauratae Mechanica. This famous work contains a description of Tycho Brahe's instruments and observatories and an account of his contributions to Astronomy.

At the time of publication Tycho Brahe had only recently left Denmark and had not yet decided to go to Prague. The number of copies printed was quite small (cf. B. Hasselberg, Vierteljahrsschrift der Astronomischen Gesellschaft 39, 180, 1904, and Lauritz Nielsen, Tycho Brahes Bogtrykkeri, København 1946). In 1901 a facsimile edition was published by B. Hasselberg. Astronomiae Instauratae Mechanica was also included in Volume V of "Tychonis Brahe Dani Opera Omnia" (edited by J. L. E. Dreyer with the collaboration of H. Ræder).

The use of the Latin language in the Astronomiae Instauratae Mechanica has probably contributed to the fact that it has become a work not often read in modern times, and a translation into English would appear to be desirable. The Royal Danish Academy of Sciences and Letters therefore decided to publish, on the occasion of the fourth centenary of the birth of Tycho Brahe, a translation from Latin into English of the principal parts of Astronomiae Instauratae Mechanica.

The present translation is the outcome of a collaboration between H. Ræder, E. Strömgren, and B. Strömgren. The Latin text was first translated into Danish by H. Ræder. The Danish text was discussed from an astronomical point of view and was then translated into English.

A thorough critical revision of the English translation was carried out by Miss Elizabeth Williamson, F. R. A. S. The editors wish to express their best thanks to Miss Williamson for her very valuable cooperation.

Finally the Latin text and the English translation were compared by H. Ræder.

The appendix was translated from Danish into English by Mr. N. Haislund, M. A. His valuable help is gratefully acknowledged.

The present translation of Astronomiae Instauratae Mechanica comprises Tycho Brahe's description of his instruments, the account of his scientific work, and finally the description of his buildings and of the island of Hven. The dedication to the Emperor Rudolph II has been omitted, and so have the poems by Rosenkrantz, Tengnagel, Chioccus, and Caukerchius, as well as the letters from Jacob Curtius and Magini.

A number of brief explanatory notes, references, and minor corrections are given in the text, always within square brackets.

The portrait of Tycho Brahe on p. 4 is a reproduction of a picture engraved by J. de Gheyn.

TYCHO BRAHE's instruments all served to determine the positions of celestial bodies. They can be divided into three groups. The first group comprises instruments for determining altitudes and azimuths, viz. various quadrants and altitude sextants, a semicircular instrument, and ruler-instruments (cf. pp. 12—51 and pp. 84—94 of this translation). The armillary instruments for measuring right ascensions and declinations, or longitudes and latitudes with respect to the ecliptic, form the second group (cf. pp. 52—67). Finally, the third group consists of a number of instruments designed for the determination of angular distances between celestial bodies. These are various sextants and the bipartite arc (cf. pp. 68—83).

The principal instruments yielding the highest accuracy were the two great revolving azimuth quadrants (cf. pp. 33 and 37), the mural quadrant (cf. p. 29), the great equatorial armillary instrument (cf. p. 65), and the triangular astronomical sextant for the determination of angular distances (cf. p. 73).

TYCHO BRAHE's methods for determining the positions of celestial bodies were similar to those of the ancients as far as the general principles are concerned (cf. J. L. E. DREYER, Tycho Brahe, Edinburgh 1890. A detailed account of TYCHO BRAHE's methods of observation is given in this work). The declinations were found from altitudes, particularly from meridian altitudes. Differences of the right ascensions of two celestial bodies were determined by the equatorial armillary instruments, or with the help of the sextants. In the latter case the declinations of the two celestial bodies had to be known. Their angular distance was observed with the sextant. The difference in right ascension could then be calculated from the spherical triangle between the two celestial objects and the pole of the equator.

Absolute right ascensions of the sun were derived from meridian altitudes. For the purpose of determining differences in right ascension of the sun and stars, Venus was used as a connecting link. Observations were made of Venus both as a morning star and as an evening star in order to eliminate the effects of refraction (cf. this translation p. 113).

In his description of the mural quadrant TYCHO BRAHE mentions two clocks, and refers to the method of determining right ascensions from the times of transit across the meridian (cf. p. 29). It appears, however, that TYCHO BRAHE was never satisfied with the accuracy of his clocks (cf. Opera Omnia II, p. 156 f.). The time was determined from the altitudes or azimuths of known stars measured with the revolvable quadrants, or by means of the equatorial armillary instruments (cf. p. 62).

TYCHO BRAHE made extensive series of observations for the purpose of determining the refraction as a function of the altitude. In this connection it must be remembered, however, that TYCHO BRAHE adopted Ptolemy's value of the solar parallax, 3′. This introduced corresponding errors in his refraction tables, and led to the adoption of different values of the refraction for the sun and for the stars (cf. p. 114).

TYCHO BRAHE introduced a greatly improved form of diopters in his instruments. Many references to this are found in the description of the instruments, and the appendix contains a separate description of the pinnules in question (cf. p. 142). In some of the instruments, such as the mural quadrant and the triangular sextant, the upper pinnule is a cylinder, so that it will serve for observations in any direction in the plane at right angles to the axis of the cylinder. In the armillary instruments a long cylindrical axis is used as the upper pinnule for the observations of longitudes, right ascensions, or hour angles. Here the line of sight is no longer restricted to the plane at right angles to the direction of the cylindrical axis, the axis being sufficiently long to allow sighting along lines making a considerable angle with this plane.

Another important innovation was the application of the method of subdivision by transversal points to circular arcs. This method is explained and discussed in detail in the appendix (cf. p. 141).

An important question in connection with Tycho Brahe's instruments is that of their size. In the description of the instruments Tycho Brahe usually gives the principal dimensions, from which most of the others may be derived, in cubits. The foot, the inch, the palm, and the span are also used, however.

The difficult question of the length of the Tychonian foot and of the passus geometricus of Tycho Brahe has been solved by N. E. Nørlund (N. E. Nørlund, De gamle danske Længdeenheder, Geodætisk Instituts Skrifter, 3. Række Bind III, København 1944, p. 32 f.). According to Nørlund the length of the Tychonian foot is 259 mm. The passus geometricus is six Tychonian feet. It has been shown by Nørlund that the passus geometricus bears a well-defined relation to the adopted diameter of the earth.

The diameter of Tycho Brahe's great brass globe (cf. p. 103) was measured by J. Picard, and by Ole Rømer and P. N. Horrebow (cf. Nørlund, loc. cit.). From their data it follows that the diameter was 149.2 cm. This is in agreement with Tycho Brahe's statement that the globe measured almost six feet in diameter.

The length of Tycho Brahe's cubit was derived by H. L. d'Arrest and by C. V. L. Charlier (N. E. Nørlund, loc. cit. p. 35) from the measured diameter of the crypt of the great revolvable steel quadrant, which Tycho Brahe states to be nine cubits (cf. p. 38). The result is about 39 cm. Since this is very close to $1\frac{1}{2}$ Tychonian feet, it is probably safe to assume that Tycho Brahe adopted the customary definition, 1 cubit = $1\frac{1}{2}$ feet (cf. H. L. d'Arrest, Astr. Nachr. 72, 209, 1868 and the references there given). It follows that 1 cubit = 388 mm.

With regard to the inch, the palm, and the span, nothing can be said with certainty. Assuming 1 foot = 4 palms = 16 inches (cf. Joh. A. Repsold, Zur Geschichte der astronomischen Messwerkzeuge, Vol. I, Leipzig 1908, p. 22) and 1 span = $\frac{3}{4}$ feet the following values are obtained: 1 inch = 16 mm, 1 palm = 65 mm, 1 span = 19 cm. These values can only serve as very rough indications of the magnitude of the units in question. It is not at all certain that they are simply related to the Tychonian foot.

With regard to other units of length used by Tycho Brahe we refer to the work of N. E. Nørlund cited above.

THE EDITORS.

CONTENTS

Appendix

QUADRANS MINOR ORICHALCICUS
INAURATUS

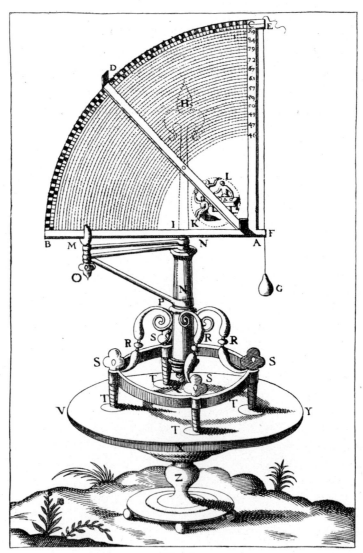

Fig. 1.

QUADRANS MINOR ORICHALCICUS INAURATUS

SMALL QUADRANT OF GILT BRASS

DESCRIPTION AND USE OF THE INSTRUMENT

A quadrant of not very large size was constructed by us many years ago. Its form appears from the figure [Fig. 1]. It consists of a massive, rather thick plate of brass, the size of which is one cubit [39 cm, cf. p. 9] from the centre A to the circumference BDC. It is gilded all over with the aid of mercury by the process of heating, so that it stays beautiful and clean and is not apt to tarnish, as is otherwise the case with brass that is not cleaned very often. The circumference BDC is divided—merely by the usual method—into 90 parts and each of these again into twelve parts, so that the latter subdivisions indicate every fifth minute of arc. Inside this division there is yet another according to the principles set forth by the famous Spanish mathematician Petrus Nonnius in his learned little book *On the Twilight* (where he attributes the method to Ptolemy which hardly carries conviction). The division is made by 44 smaller quadrants being drawn inside the outermost, one after another. The outermost of these must be divided into 89 parts, the next one into 88, the third into 87, and so forth, until the last and innermost is reached, which is to have 46 parts, as can be seen fairly well from the figure. The alidade DA has pinnules at A and D, made in the usual way with holes. On the lower pinnule at A slits parallel to the sides of the upper one are sometimes used, as is our custom, and in this way it is possible to point more easily and with greater accuracy. On the back of it a plumb line EFG is hung, in order to make it possible to see, with its aid, if the position of the quadrant is correct so that the lower side AB is quite horizontal, and the other side AC is pointed exactly towards the zenith, and the plane of the whole quadrant coincides with the plane of a vertical circle. The adjustment of the quadrant is carried out, partly by means of some screws near the base of the instrument, denoted by the letter S, partly by a screw at OM by which the quadrant proper can be raised or lowered, until the plumb line shows that it has the right position. The quadrant rests on a base NMOPQRST which, like the rest of the equipment, is made entirely of pure iron, where it is fastened to the quadrant on the back at

H. Near N this support is movable to some extent, so that the quadrant can be moved up and down with the aid of the screw OM, for the iron rods MN and ON can be contracted or extended with the aid of the screw OM already mentioned, and in this way it is possible to raise or lower the quadrant a little, as needed. It is also possible to turn it around in a hollow tube in any direction that might be desired, the whole lower part of the base, denoted by the letters RSQT, hereby remaining fixed, however. This lower part has supports of the shape shown in the figure, so that the quadrant is fixed steadily to its four screws, denoted by the letters ST. And these screws control the whole instrument, as already mentioned, for getting it into adjustment. The screws rest on iron plates at T. While the latter remain fixed on a table VXYZ, the screws can be turned as desired. So much for the quadrant and its base in general.

But the picture, which is fairly well seen in the space between the centre and the innermost quadrant arc, surrounded by a circle LK, has been modelled as an ornament, and also in order that its inscription might offer some instruction. This space would otherwise be empty. In the picture one sees (let me state that also on this occasion) a young man, wreathed by a laurel branch, sitting on a square stone near a tree which on one side is green and leafy. In one hand he is holding a celestial globe, in the other a book, and he is stretching his feet into green grass and herbs that cover the root of the tree. On the other, left, side of the tree the root is dried up and the branches withered and without leaves. Between them is a table covered with some of the things valued by men on this earthly stage, such as a box filled with coins, sceptres, crowns, coats of arms, golden chains, gems, finery, goblets, cards and dice, and the like. Around all this a skeleton, representing Death, is stretching its hands and feet, as if trying to snatch it. But above the whole of the picture is a hemistich, explaining the allegorical meaning: "By spirit we live, the rest will belong to death". This is placed in such a way that the first part of the hemistich, on the right, green side of the tree, where the philosophizing young man is sitting, is hanging down from the branches as on a slip of paper, while the rest of the hemistich is on the other side. My intention has been to suggest that sure science, especially the sublime knowledge of celestial things, bestows eternal life and remembrance on this earth, while everything else is worthless and transient, perishing with the human body. But when we consider the eternity of heaven, then the very things that are now on the green side of the tree pass over on to the other side; for between the finite and the infinite there is no relation. And then the hemistich of the inscription is changed and now runs as follows: "In Christ we live, the rest will belong to death", so that the first part corresponds to the green tree, and the second to that which is withered. But within the green picture of the tree there is an inscription alluding to the life and teachings of Christ. The rest remains unchanged as before, only that human sciences and inventions now point to the back and left side of the tree, viz. the withered side. With this we indicate that nothing can make man happy and give him eternal immortality except the merits of Christ, God's son and our Saviour, and the contemplation of his life and teaching. All this I have wished to present here in detail on account of the added picture, even though it is perhaps irrelevant. On the back of the quadrant is a table with engraved numbers, which with the greatest ease show the correspondence between each single point of the Nonnian divisions mentioned above and the required altitudes.

The use of this quadrant is for finding the altitudes of the stars and of the sun and moon in such cases when complete accuracy is not necessary, a value with an error less than two or three minutes being sufficient. The plane of the quadrant is then turned until it passes through the star to be observed. The orientation of the quadrant is corrected with the aid of the screws, as described above, until the plumb line shows that everything is correct. Next, the alidade AD is raised or lowered until the star is seen through the holes or slits of the pinnules, or the light of the sun just shines through them. Then it is clamped at the other end near D, where it is provided with a small screw that is not visible in the figure. In this way the outermost end of the alidade will indicate on the outer rim, where the common divisions are situated, the required altitude with an accuracy of five minutes. And of these it is possible to perceive one-half, or one-third, if the reading is carefully made. But if one desires to use in addition the Nonnian divisions, then one has to watch whether the alidade passes some point or other among the divisions, no matter in which, and find by counting what is the number of the particular point in the row of divisions, and what is the total number of points in that row. With these two figures one then enters the table engraved on the back of the quadrant and thus the degrees and minutes of the measured altitude are obtained in the usual way from the two figures. The same end can be attained without the use of a table by proportions without much labour, the number of divisional points in the row to which the point that is touched by the alidade belongs being put in the first place, 90 degrees in the second, and the number of the point mentioned in its row, counted from the beginning of the division to the alidade, in the third place. In this way the fourth number found by the usual procedure of calculation will give the quantity required. This Nonnian method, however, is insufficient in practice, and experience will show that the promised accuracy is not in fact obtained by it.

QUADRANS MEDIOCRIS ORICHAL-
CICUS AZIMUTHALIS

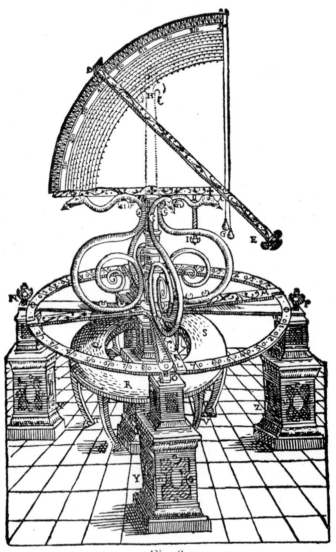

Fig. 2.

QUADRANS MEDIOCRIS ORICHALCICUS AZIMUTHALIS

MEDIUM SIZED AZIMUTH QUADRANT OF BRASS

DESCRIPTION AND USE OF THE INSTRUMENT

This quadrant ABC [cf. Fig. 2; the letters in this figure do not in all cases correspond to those in the text], which is made of a solid brass plate, has a size of one and a half cubits [58 cm, cf. p. 9] from its centre to its circumference AB. The thickness is about one-half of an inch [cf. p. 9]. Within the circumference it contains not only our usual division with lines and transversal points (as described elsewhere), but also the division due to Nonnius, the famous Spanish mathematician, and published by him in his learned little book *On the Twilight*. I have mentioned it in the description of the preceding instrument, but here it is extended in another and more practical way, so that it contains a greater number of subdivisions, particularly corresponding to such numbers as can be conveniently divided by several integers. In that respect the Nonnian division involved great difficulties, as it is already insufficient to indicate all the minutes of the quadrant, to say nothing of the determination of the seconds, which was Nonnius' intention. This can be done by calculation rather than in a mechanical way. Indeed it often happens that beginners thus make a mistake in this art. On the back of the quadrant is an engraved table, explaining the divisions and making possible their use with the greatest ease and without further calculation.

The alidade DE of the instrument is made entirely of steel, in order always to remain straight, but in addition it is gilded to prevent rusting. At DE it has two pinnules of brass, of which the lower one at E is provided with slits parallel to the upper pinnule at D. The observer has to place his eye against the former, in order that he may the more accurately and from a central point distinguish the stars around the forward pinnule without any uncertainty. We have made use of this method with nearly all our instruments. The alidade proper has, on purpose, been made longer than the radius of the quadrant at AE, the intention being partly to make it easier to raise or lower the alidade, grasping it with the fingers at the lower end near E, until the precise altitude and also the azimuth of the star to be observed have been found. Also the alidade remains in position wherever it is placed, a fine steel spring on the other side of the quadrant at D holding it, in order that the observation may be the more accurate and convenient. In this way one obtains, as a rule, the same result as if the radius of the quadrant were of the length DE. Add to this that the supports below will not inconvenience the observer, and that the instrument becomes easier to handle. This explanation of the quadrant proper must now suffice. With regard to the supports mentioned the facts are as follows. In the first place the quadrant itself which is fastened to a cylindrical piece of strong iron with the aid of a small screw at H (so that it can be removed if desired), can be turned around in a tube. On the outside the latter is surrounded by the winding serpents seen in the figure [Figure 2], which serve the double purpose of support and decoration. Below the tube has another alidade, seen at K and M, which together with the plane of the quadrant can be turned on the steel azimuth horizon NOP in any direction. Carrying out this operation the alidade with its pointer K shows the azimuth of the observed star as well as the altitude, in such a way that the altitudes are measured on the quadrant above, and the azimuths on the said azimuth circle. The three screws that can be seen near the letters mentioned, together with a fourth one, which is invisible on the other side, make it possible to adjust the steel horizon to coincide with the plane of the true horizon, and to adjust the quadrant above, so that it is at right angles to the plane of the horizon and both its sides aligned towards the zenith. In addition there is also another screw at I, which can correct it to within very small deviations, if necessary, so that the quadrant, whatever its position may be, will accurately coincide with the plane of any vertical circle. Furthermore, these steel screws that carry the entire instrument rest on four marble pillars, three of which are visible and denoted by the letters XYZ. The fourth, on the farther side, is similar to these, but nearly invisible. Finally inside these four pillars there is a stool, or base, denoted by QRS, on to which one can mount, after the observation has been made, in order to read off and record accurately and conveniently the altitude observed on the circumference of the quadrant. These specifications of the construction of the instrument must now suffice. If there be some further details, information about which is desired, these can easily be found out by examining the figure with one's own eyes and with great attention.

The use of the instrument is very comprehensive and includes all cases where observed altitudes and azimuths of a planet or a fixed star can by trigonometry yield a numerical solution conforming to the requirements of observational astronomy. Concerning this question astronomical scientific literature should be consulted, and also that which we ourselves have written on the subject here and there in our books, when this was required by the context, particularly in the second volume of the *Progymnasmata astronomica*, where a clear description of the comet of the year 1577 is given. For in making the observations of this comet, which are presented in the book mentioned and made use of in the demonstration, this quadrant was especially useful, since I did not at the time possess the other larger, and differently constructed ones that were made later. This one was good enough, however, since by its aid it was possible to distinguish sufficiently between the minutes of arc both of altitude and of azimuth. The instrument is also explained towards the end of the book mentioned. On p. 461 and the three following pages [Opera Omnia IV, 371 f.] this quadrant is described in more detail in various respects, and furthermore a description, illustrated by a careful drawing, is given of the very convenient and very accurate method of dividing the circumference by means of transversal points, which we were the first to apply to circular arcs. Its diopter also is illustrated and described there on p. 462, and a clear exposition is given of the construction of the pinnules and the slits, which I frequently speak of, and all the rest pertaining to this subject. To this I therefore refer the interested reader, and there he will also find more about the mechanical construction of this and other instruments, which could not be dealt with here for lack of space. And all that has been set forth there concerning graduation and the placing of the pinnules is also valid for all other instruments in which these are to be used, so that it is not necessary for us to trouble ourselves by repeating it here and in other places. Only this I wish to state here with regard both to this instrument and to the others, namely, that all of it has to be as nearly perfect as is possible in every respect and that, therefore, one should employ skilful craftsmen, who know how to carry out this sort of work artfully, or else can learn how to do it. And even if they cannot perhaps do it all perfectly the first time, the constructor must not let himself be discouraged, but have the work repeated and improve the defects in every way, until none is left. The observations themselves will make this sufficiently clear to the expert, provided they are varied. Consequently we have remade most of the instruments described in this book more than once, not without great expense. We have indeed had instruments completely rebuilt. We have also built mills, worked partly by horses, partly by water power, for the purpose of turning the instruments, although this procedure was generally useless. We incurred many other expenses in this connexion, a fact which is not so easily appreciated by mere inspection of the instruments themselves.

QUADRANS ALIUS ORICHALCICUS
ETIAM AZIMUTHALIS

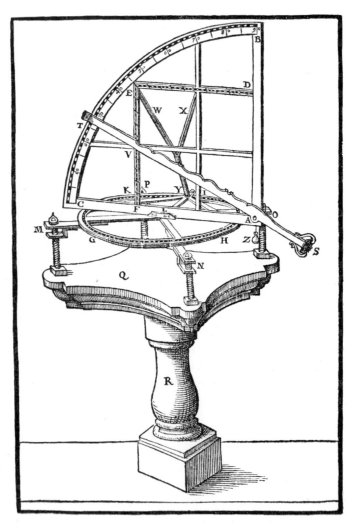

Fig. 3.

QUADRANS ALIUS ORICHALCICUS ETIAM AZIMUTHALIS

ANOTHER AZIMUTH QUADRANT OF BRASS

DESCRIPTION AND USE OF THE INSTRUMENT

This quadrant ABC also consists of solid brass, but it has been constructed as in the figure [Fig. 3]. Below it has a horizon GHIK indicating the azimuth, cast of solid brass. The various parts of the instrument, which we are going to explain separately, are constructed as follows. The length from the centre A to B or C is one and a half cubits [58 cm, cf. p. 9]. The circumference BC is as before divided into single minutes with the aid of transversal points according to our usual custom, but it is not divided by another method also, as was the case with the previous instrument, the breadth of the rim being insufficient for this. Still it is about two inches wide [cf. p. 9] and is able to show, by the transversal points, each single minute. The square ADEF seen in the plane of the quadrant, and the crossed braces, have been put in only for support and to give greater security, but nevertheless the square may also be of use in making geometrical measurements of the height and breadth of objects seen on the terrestrial surface and built upon it through the efforts of men just as the instrument called *The Geometrical Square* by Peurbach can serve this or similar purposes. This subject has been demonstrated and explained by the excellent man just mentioned, in a special little book, and it has also been dealt with, although not in equal detail, by those who describe an astrolabe, especially its so-called dorsum, or back. A second added piece that is visible near the one just referred to, and which one has to imagine on the back of the quadrant, Y-shaped and denoted by the letters WXY, serves the purpose of putting the plane of the quadrant proper at right angles to the horizon upon which it turns, however it may be turned around. Further, a small screw at Y, where this piece joins the horizontal circle, clamps the quadrant rigidly in a permanent position when desired, so that the azimuth reading can be correctly made. At the same point a bar from the centre L to the screw Y connects one end of the brace with the lower and middle part of the quadrant, in order that

4

it all hold so much the more solidly together and move together when the instrument is turned. Furthermore a small spring is placed below, near the screw, so that the quadrant will stay in any position without shifting in the least. The fact that this quadrant is not solid all through its plane, but has the, mostly square, spaces shown in the figure, has the advantage that it is lighter, and therefore easier both to operate, and to transport from one place to another. With a view to this, it is also put together from different parts, but this we shall discuss in more detail below. The alidade carrying pinnules we shall speak about, after explaining, first, a little about the azimuthal horizon. These pinnules are used for observing altitude as well as azimuth. That is why the alidade with its somewhat oblong and broad surface lies everywhere close to the plane of the quadrant, so that the lowest part of it, AS, which projects over the quadrant, also accurately follows the same plane, and so that, further, the pinnules have the same distance from it, and are also at right angles to it. Otherwise it would not be possible to determine the azimuths accurately, let alone the altitudes. The azimuthal horizon, which I have mentioned, and which is below the quadrant and also carries it, is denoted by GHIK. It is provided with braces crossing each other at right angles to make it the more rigid, so that the quadrant as a whole will turn about the point where the braces cross, namely the centre of the horizontal circle mentioned, in a tube that is placed at this point. At the endpoints of the braces are four screws MNOP, with the aid of which the whole horizon, and the quadrant proper, which rests upon it, can be set so that the latter coincides with the plane of any vertical circle, while the former falls in the plane of the horizon. In this way they can be used for their true purpose, for measuring altitude and azimuth. The alidade SVT mentioned above, which is placed on the quadrant proper, is constructed in the same way as for the previous instrument as far as the diopters and pinnules are concerned, but there are two handles below near the diopter S, by which one can easily raise or lower the alidade, as required by the altitude to be observed. The handles also serve as counterweights holding the other end TA of the alidade approximately in equilibrium. The whole instrument rests upon a four cornered stone which for the sake of convenience is somewhat hollowed out on the sides. It is denoted by the letter Q. The stone in its turn rests solidly on a stone pillar R, as appears quite clearly from the figure. This quadrant has the constructional advantage in comparison with the previous one that the horizontal plane upon which it rests, as well as the rest of the instrument, can be taken apart conveniently, and be put together again, so that it is suited for transport from one place to another in a case into which it fits. Add to this that it does not consist of so many separate pieces as the previous one, and that these pieces can easily be taken apart and put together again as before, with the aid of small screws in various places. Therefore I generally refer to this as the portable azimuth quadrant.

The use of the instrument is similar to that of the previous one as regards the requirements of observed altitudes and azimuths which by geometrical methods yield numerical solutions. None the less it should be emphasized, that one cannot depend entirely on these two quadrants, when a very accurate observation, to a fraction of a minute, is required. I am here thinking of the observations that serve to determine the orbit of the sun, where the question is of very small quantities, and where an accuracy of one-sixth, or at least one-third of a minute of arc is required. Such small instruments, measuring not more than one, or one and a half cubits [39 cm, or 58 cm, cf. p. 9] are unable to yield such an accuracy. Let us therefore, now, pass to the larger instruments which are better suited for this sort of observation, instruments which can give the accuracy required in the case of the sun, and, in addition, are also suited for the investigation of very small parallaxes and possible differences in any celestial phenomenon, and which can reveal with the highest accuracy many other things by observations of planets as well as fixed stars. If the reader is interested, he may find examples of such parallaxes in the second volume of our *Astronomiae instaurandae Progymnasmata,* where, both in the first and the second part, I deal carefully with the seven comets that have appeared during these twenty years, and with the greatest thoroughness examine their parallaxes, as far as they could be ascertained, and where I give mathematical and irrefutable proof that they have all been permanently in the ethereal regions far beyond the moon. It is true that among those belonging to the school of Aristotle there are many who are unwilling to accept this truth more than sufficiently proved, as is also otherwise often the case with the different opinions of men. The truth, however, must not be hidden. Then those who recognize it, and are willing to do so, may believe in it.

SEXTANS ASTRONOMICUS, PROUT
ALTITUDINIBUS INSERVIT

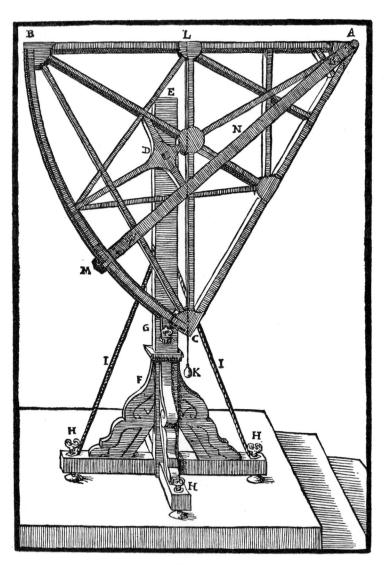

Fig. 4.

SEXTANS ASTRONOMICUS, PROUT ALTITU-
DINIBUS INSERVIT

ASTRONOMICAL SEXTANT FOR MEASURING ALTITUDES

DESCRIPTION AND USE OF THE INSTRUMENT

The astronomical sextant instrument, which is particularly convenient in use, was first invented by myself, about twenty years ago. I have even given it this name, because its circumference comprises one-sixth of a circle. It is entirely sufficient for observations, which can as a rule be made in this way, and it does not increase the difficulties by being too big. It is true that there are others, who have claimed later on that they invented it, and who have introduced certain modifications of the form, just as is the case with several other inventions of mine, which certain people both in Germany and elsewhere have not been ashamed to appropriate. In the course of time I have constructed three instruments of this type (not to speak of various others for the same purpose). They are similar as far as the outer borders and pinnules are concerned, but differ in the construction of the inner framework, which has been adapted to the particular purpose. The instrument to be described now [Fig. 4], was, with regard to the framework mentioned, of quite simple construction, consisting of a rather small number of beams, because I had planned the construction in such a way that it would be easy to take the instrument to pieces and put it together again in other places with the aid of screws, so that it could be put into a case together with its base, which could also be taken apart, and thus be transported to other places, not only by sea in a ship (which would be the safest), but also by land in a carriage. In this way the altitude of the pole in different countries might be examined exactly. The fact is that this instrument is suited not only for the angular distances of the sun and the stars, but also for their altitudes, which this instrument (as I have said) is well suited to determine. When the instrument is to be used for finding altitudes, it is placed as shown [in Fig. 4]. Now I shall explain, first, its construction, and then briefly indicate its use. This sextant ABC is on all sides completely covered with brass plates, and so ingeniously that one would think that it was cast from solid brass, since not a single crack can be seen where the plates meet. The distance from the centre to the circumference is four cubits [155 cm, cf. p. 9]. At the centre is placed a cylinder A, with the aid of which the observations are made by means of the lower pinnule M of the alidade ANM. This pinnule has two slits with a mutual distance as required by the diameter of the cylinder, in order that the observation may be made in parallel lines on both sides, and the star be observed centrally without any uncertainty. The circumference BC is divided by transversal points as has been our custom with other instruments, this method being in our experience the most practical, convenient and free from error. The method is explained in greater detail towards the end of the book, quoted already, on the comet of the year 1577. This method has been appropriated by others in Germany, after Wittich, who had seen it with me, disclosed it in Cassel together with the arrangement of the pinnules, and perhaps also offered it for sale, as if it belonged to him. It should be mentioned, however, that when the sun's altitude is to be observed, the most practical procedure is to place an oblong rectangular tube on the alidade itself with its diopters and pinnules, in order to distinguish the shadow accurately. This tube must be constructed out of light material, in order not to influence the alidade and its pinnules by its weight. The tube should leave open a small space, like a slit, at the cylinder A, above as well as below it, so that the solar rays, penetrating on both sides, can show the square shadow of the cylinder the more clearly on the inner side of the lower pinnule, within the square figure corresponding to the shadow. For this reason there must be an opening at this place, through which one can look conveniently and clearly, as it is our custom to do in other cases also in solar observations, in order that the boundary of light and shadow may appear the more clearly. This instrument can be taken apart and put together with the aid of strong screws ABCDL, and in several other places not indicated by letters. The arc and the bar BC subtending it cannot be taken apart but remain connected, in order that this arc shall not lose the accurate position of its circumference. Further the instrument has a base, on to which it is fastened when altitudes are to be observed with it (as is the case here). It is denoted by EGH, and in it there is a round hole, in which the instrument is fastened with the aid of a bolt at D. Having been moved to and fro the instrument is finally fastened below by a screw G, a plumb-line fastened near L indicating below at C, the endpoint of the divided arc, that the side AB is exactly parallel to the horizon. The point L, however, from where a thin brass wire is hanging down, is located exactly half-way between the center A and one endpoint B of the circumference. In this way an isosceles [equilateral] triangle ABC is produced. The fact that the radius of the circle and the chord subtending one-sixth of the circumference are equal, is known from the elements of geometry. Now, since the line CL is at right angles to the line AB, and the plumb-line is adjusted to coincide with the line CL, the latter must necessarily point towards the zenith, while the former is parallel to the plane of the horizon. The instrument can thus be adjusted for the determination of altitudes as accurately as if a whole quadrant were being used. The base, or support, is made of strong wood of a form that can be seen [from Figure 4].

Inside, it is for the most part hollow, in order that it should not through excessive weight render transport difficult. Nevertheless some iron mountings are placed here and there in places where they are needed, for protection against shock and damage. Furthermore three oblong iron braces run from the centre to the end-points of the feet of the base. Two of them are denoted by IH, while the third is behind the instrument and invisible. They can be removed or put on with the aid of screws belonging to them. There are, further, four steel screws that support the whole instrument. Three of these are denoted by the letter H, while the fourth, which is behind, is invisible. The screws make it possible to adjust the instrument simply and securely. They turn on top of some small metal plates, in order not, by their weight and with their points, to exert uneven pressure on the floor upon which they rest. The observer turns them, until he finds with the aid of the plumb-line that the instrument is adjusted so as to correspond to the plane of some vertical circle.

The use of the instrument, when treated in the way described, is for measuring all altitudes, of the sun and the moon as well as of planets and fixed stars, within an accuracy of one-third, or one-fourth, of a minute of arc, so long as they do not extend over more than one-sixth of the sky. Indeed, it is possible with this instrument to include the rest of the sky, provided the sextant is fixed in a different way, namely so that AC points towards the zenith. Only altitudes are obtained in this fashion, however, not azimuths as well. This sextant is particularly well suited for taking accurately, not only altitudes, but also angular distances between the stars. No difficulty or uncertainty is involved in this work, since the sextant consists of a few separate pieces only which, as mentioned already, are rigidly joined together, in order that they should not shift from their proper place during the observation. The instrument has the further advantage, as I have hinted before, that it can easily be transported to other places without danger of damage or other inconveniences. As far as possible one should see to it that such is the case for some instruments, in order to be independent of place. An astronomer, more than the student of other branches of knowledge, has to be a citizen of the world, and consider every place to which circumstances or necessity might lead him as his native country.

QUADRANS MURALIS SIVE TICHO-
NICUS

Fig. 5.

QUADRANS MURALIS SIVE TICHONICUS

THE MURAL, OR TYCHONIAN, QUADRANT

DESCRIPTION AND USE OF THE INSTRUMENT

We also had a very large quadrant made, which is shown here [Fig. 5] denoted by BDEC. It is called Mural, or Tichonicus, after the wall on which it is fixed. It is cast from solid brass and very finely polished. It is five inches wide and two inches thick, and the circumference is so large that it corresponds to a radius of nearly five cubits [194 cm, cf. p. 9]. Its degrees are in consequence extremely large and every single minute can be divided again into six subdivisions; thus ten seconds of arc are plainly distinguishable and even half this, or five seconds of arc, can be read without difficulty. This is all done by means of transversal points drawn according to our usual method.

This quadrant is fastened to a wall MPQ, the plane of which points exactly towards the south. The fastening is by strong screws, so that the quadrant cannot be forced out of its proper position, which has been determined beforehand so that it corresponds entirely to the quadrant of the celestial meridian from the horizon to the zenith, in such a way, however, that it is exactly opposite to the latter. On another wall LMNB, which is at right angles to the first, pointing exactly east and west, is a brass cylinder, placed above, over the centre of the quadrant. The brass cylinder is gilded in order not to be damaged by the effects of the air, or otherwise soiled. It is seen near the letter A in a square hole in the same wall, which can be opened or closed with the aid of a shutter fitting into it. In this way it is possible when the sky is clear, to sight along both sides of the cylinder mentioned, and for this the pinnules near D or E are used. In fact this quadrant has two pinnules, so that either of them may be used, as desired, according to which one is best suited for the particular altitude that is to be measured. Each of them has a square plane, one hand broad [cf. p. 9]. This corresponds exactly to the diameter of the cylinder mentioned above, so that one can aim through the parallel slits, which are placed on the pinnules on all four sides, in case it is intended to determine at the same time both the altitude and the transit over the meridian. If, however, the altitude alone is required, the observer, who is shown near F, makes the observation through the upper and the lower slit, and the corresponding sides of the cylinder, and then dictates the measured altitude to a second collaborator, who is sitting at the table G with a light, in order that he may enter the result in the ledger of observations. In order that the time of observation, and the very moment of the transit over the meridian may also be noted, a third collaborator, denoted by H, watches the clocks I and K, when the observer at F gives a signal, and the time is also entered in the ledger by the person sitting at G. The clocks mentioned are constructed in such a way, that they give not only the single minutes, but also the seconds, with the greatest possible accuracy, and imitating the uniform rotation of the heavens. Although it is difficult to make the clocks do this, one can, by exercising great care, to a certain degree attain this end. Also, if an error has crept in, it can be noted and corrected. Therefore it is necessary to have two clocks of this kind so that one can correct the other if necessary. We have at our disposal four such clocks. One of these, the largest, manages the whole business with the aid of three wheels, of which the largest, cast from solid pure brass, has 1200 teeth. The diameter of this wheel is two cubits [78 cm, cf. p. 9], from which the rest can be calculated. The three other clocks are smaller, and need more wheels. The construction of all these clocks we shall, God willing, describe on another occasion. The pictures which can be seen within the circumference of the quadrant are only added for the sake of ornament, and in order that the space in the middle should not be empty and useless. It will not be out of place, however, to give a brief explanation of these, although they are not quite relevant. Beneath the letter T is a painted portrait of myself, seated on a chair at a table in a long cloak reaching to the feet, in a somewhat reclining position, and stretching out the right hand in the direction of the cylinder, as if pointing towards it. The other hand is resting on the table beside a book and a few other objects, as if I were indicating to my collaborators what is to be observed, and for what purpose the observations are made. This portrait was painted with great skill by the distinguished artist Thobias Gemperlin (whom I had at one time taken with me from Augsburg to Denmark). The likeness could hardly be more striking, and the height and stature of the body is rendered very realistically. Above the head near X a gilded brass globe is mounted, in the interior of which wheels are ingeniously placed, so that it can revolve and imitate the diurnal rotation, and also represent the course of the sun and the moon in the opposite direction as seen from the poles of the ecliptic, so that even the changing phases of the moon, with its growing and diminishing light, are shown. The sun, turning inside 24 hour circles, according to the diurnal revolution around the equatorial axis, in addition to its own motion, indicates the single hours of the day, and also the times of sunrise and sunset as well as the transits over the meridian, to the south and north. This ingenious mechanism, which I invented myself and had constructed at my own expense, I humbly presented in the year 1590 [should be 1592] to His Majesty Christian, at the time King Elect, my most gracious lord, when seven years ago, in his fourteenth year, he was good enough graciously to visit me at Uraniborg on the island of Hven, accompanied by three of the noblest Councillors of the Realm, who at the time were at the head of the government, as well as by the rest of the Royal Household. This globe is still in his possession. But His Majesty, the King Elect, graciously presented to me in return a golden chain, a magnificent work of art, of the kind which he was at the time wont to wear, beautifully worked and adorned with his own portrait. Above this globe, which I have just described, part of my library is represented at the letter V. At the letters Y and Z two portraits are hanging solidly mounted within a round frame. One of them represents the mighty King of the Danes, His Majesty King Frederick II, of illustrious memory, the other Her Majesty Queen Sophie, his high consort, those who always with royal and gracious favour supported me and my work. The other paintings that can be seen in the inner space are, first, above at the figures 1, 2, 3, 4 some of my instruments which are represented there. Further, below this framework is shown my study. Here some tables are standing near 5 and 8, at which my astronomical assistants are generally occupied with calculations or other tasks of this kind. In the actual study there were four such tables. I used to keep at least six or eight, sometimes ten or twelve such collaborators, who came to me from all directions, and in addition a few boys and youths of the same kind. Between these tables at 6 and 7 one sees, behind a pillar, in the middle of the round study, the very large brass globe of six feet diameter [the diameter was 149 cm, cf. p. 9] which I shall depict and explain later on in the right place [cf. p. 9]. Finally, below all this, at 9, 10, and 11, is seen my chemical laboratory, which was all in an underground basement. Here I had had arranged 16 chemical furnaces of different kinds and forms. From my youth I have been interested in this study, no less than in Astronomy, and I have cultivated it with great diligence and no small expense. In the last space, at the number 12, one of my hounds is lying at my feet. This dog was exceptionally faithful and sagacious and is shown in shape and size much as he was in life, a symbol not only of his noble race but also of sagacity and fidelity. This gives you a summary representation of the whole picture, as far as it was possible to render it on so small a scale. Three different distinguished artists made these paintings for me. My portrait was painted by the artist from Augsburg mentioned, the buildings and that which is inside them was done by my architect Johannes Stenwinckel of Emden. The representation above of landscapes and mountains, however, in which a sunset is also seen, was added by the royal Kronborg-artist Johannes of Antwerp. Each of the three artists mentioned has distinguished himself beyond others in the particular field in which he is here exemplified. Finally there is above at RS an inscription over the portrait and the whole painting, as you can see.

The use of the large quadrant is for determining the altitudes of the stars within one-sixth of a minute, by sighting through the upper and lower slits of one of the pinnules and along the two corresponding sides of the cylinder, and reading off the altitude on the outer rim of the quadrant in accordance with the position of this pinnule. It is also possible to find the moment of transit over the meridian by double sights with the pinnules and the cylinder, by using the accurate clocks that I have spoken about. The method by which the position of a star can be found from the given altitude, and the moment of transit over the meridian, by making use of the course of the sun, is well-known to astronomers. I have had great faith in this quadrant, when the question was that of determining the course of the sun from its altitude in the meridian, the rectangular shadow of the cylinder falling on the interior of one of the pinnules in a space, also rectangular, into which the shadow fitted exactly. Nevertheless I have also consulted other large quadrants, in order to avoid the least suspicion of error in such delicate investigations.

QUADRANS VOLUBILIS AZIMU-
THALIS

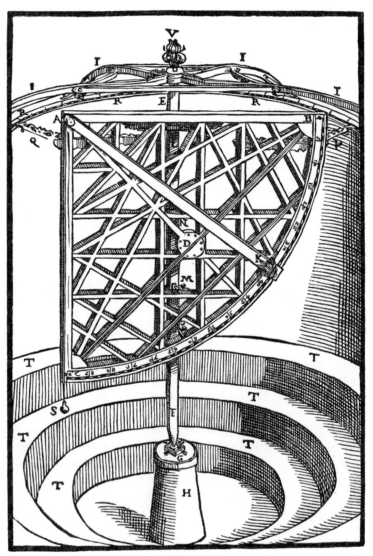

Fig. 6.

QUADRANS VOLUBILIS AZIMUTHALIS

REVOLVING AZIMUTH QUADRANT

DESCRIPTION AND USE OF THE INSTRUMENT

A revolving quadrant, which can be used for determining not only altitudes, like the previous sextant, but also, most accurately, azimuths, has been constructed by us, of an appearance as seen in the figure [Fig. 6]. From the centre A to the circumference B, or C, it measures four cubits [155 cm, cf. p. 9]. The circumference is provided by means of transversal points with a subdivision which is so fine that one-quarter of a minute can be distinguished if the sighting is carefully made, and the eye held at the pinnule K, while the alidade AK is moved until the star to be observed shines equally brightly on both sides of the cylinder A. Then the instrument shows the required altitude with the aid of the alidade, where the latter cuts the divisions at K. The pointer Q, which points towards the azimuth arc, denoted by R, simultaneously indicates the azimuths. The framework seen in the plane of the quadrant is arranged in various ways so as to keep it rigidly and permanently in its plane, and moreover entirely in its proper shape. The rim upon which the divisions are placed is completely covered with brass plates. All such pieces of the quadrant, for which this might be required, have also been covered with steel or brass. The quadrant is fastened to a strong, quadrilateral iron pillar LMN. Together with this it can be turned around, with the greatest ease, in any desired direction. The iron pillar mentioned is round on top and can turn within a hole in a dense iron grid, which is connected crosswise with a round wall that forms a small tower, or crypt, in which the instrument was kept. Below at G, where this same pillar ends in a rounded steel point, it can turn in a small hole, similarly shaped. The pillar turns on a small steel plate that can be moved, with the aid of four small screws placed around it, in any required direction, until both plumb-lines of the quadrant, which hang down from A and end at S, adjust the plane as well as the dorsum, or back, of the quadrant in such a way that it is found to coincide exactly with any vertical circle. Once this has been done, and the quadrant has been adjusted with diligence in all azimuth directions and kept in position with the aid of the requisite screws, the plumb-lines need only be briefly

5

watched to see whether the quadrant has moved a little out of its correct position. This cannot happen, however, unless it is subject to unexpected violence, and in that case it is easy to readjust the instrument in the way described. It stands very rigidly on the round stone H, which is solid and dug deeply into the ground on to another stone foundation. The iron grid mentioned, which is arranged crosswise above, and rests upon a solid wall, does not permit the iron pillar, to which the quadrant is fastened, to shift in the least out of the hole in its centre.

The round wall that corresponds exactly to the circumference of a circle has a diameter of about six cubits [233 cm, cf. p. 9] in order that there should be sufficient space between the circumference of the quadrant and the inner side of the crypt, for the observer to move around conveniently. The wall carries a solid circle covered with brass plates, upon which it shows the azimuths all around the horizon to which it is parallel. It is divided into minutes and immovably fixed. The zero point of the azimuths, which depends upon the meridian line, is determined with such care and accuracy that the observer will not err by a single minute. The meridian line we ourselves determined by using a new method that is far more reliable than any one used before, namely, with the aid of the pole star, when it is at greatest elongation from the meridian, on either side of it, and apparently for a brief interval remains in the same azimuth. This is a simple and infallible method, which I have devised. It was certainly worth the trouble, for where astronomical observations are concerned there is not much that can be done as long as the meridian line has not been very accurately determined. The observations with the instrument are made in the following way. It can be directed towards any star that is visible in the sky by turning the plane of the quadrant, and raising or lowering the alidade with its pinnules, until the star in question is seen accurately through the slits of the pinnule near the eye, first through the upper slit and along the upper rim of the cylinder, and then in the same way through the lower slit, sighting along the lower rim. The alidade then, with the greatest accuracy, indicates the required altitude of the star at the point where it cuts the divided limb at K. If it is desired by the same operation to find the azimuth of the star also, then the quadrant should for a brief moment be turned slightly to and fro on its pillar, until the same star is seen simultaneously through both side slits and along both sides of the cylinder. Then the index Q will at the same time indicate the exact azimuth on the horizontal circle. Since, however, it is not very easy to distinguish these two simultaneously on account of the continuous and rapid motion of the sky, the best method is to set the index Q at some fixed azimuth approached by the star, and then wait until the azimuth is reached by the star as a consequence of the diurnal rotation of the universe. At this very moment the altitude is determined by moving the diopter of the alidade up and down. This can be done without much trouble.

The use of this instrument is the same as that of other instruments serving the determination of altitudes and azimuths. In comparison with these it has, however, the advantage that it easily makes possible determinations of the quantities mentioned, of the highest accuracy and certainty, even within one-quarter of a minute of arc. This is not possible with those described before, partly on account of their small size, partly because they are not built in such an ingenious way, nor so convenient to use. An astronomer, therefore, ought to consider this construction as particularly commendable. To make the use of the instrument more convenient, as regards the observations as well as the reading of the circles, the steps denoted by T, which surround it, give an elevation corresponding to that of the quadrant. Thus, when the observer is standing on the highest step, he can observe a star near the horizon. While sitting on the lowest step, he can observe stars near the zenith, and similarly for all stars in between. This instrument with its small crypt-turret is covered on top by a roof, made of small, smooth beams, ingeniously joined together and connected, below the horizontal top of the wall and outside the azimuth circle, by a strong, round wooden ring. Hidden inside this ring are wheels, placed opposite each other in four places. With the aid of these wheels the roof can be turned around, with little effort, as may be desired. In this way the two oblong windows, which are placed in the roof opposite each other, and which are likewise formed of small beams, can be turned towards any star that is to be observed. These windows are shut when the observations are finished, in order that the instrument should be protected against damage from the air, and against rain and wind. This should be done, as far as possible, with the other instruments also, since they are very valuable and are easily damaged if not protected against violence as well as dirt and the influence of the elements.

QUADRANS MAGNUS CHALIBEUS,
IN QUADRATO ETIAM CHALIBEO COMPREHENSUS,
UNAQUE AZIMUTHALIS

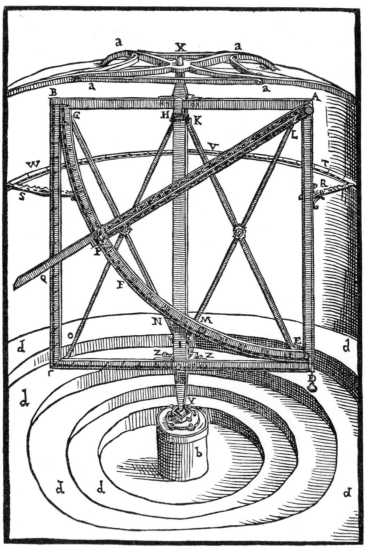

Fig. 7.

QUADRANS MAGNUS CHALIBEUS, IN QUADRATO ETIAM CHALIBEO COMPREHENSUS, UNAQUE AZIMUTHALIS

GREAT STEEL QUADRANT, INSCRIBED IN A SQUARE, ALSO OF STEEL, AND REVOLVING IN AZIMUTH

DESCRIPTION AND USE OF THE INSTRUMENT

This quadrant, which is entirely made of solid steel, and further surrounded with a steel square, serves the same purpose as the previous one, with even greater accuracy, since it is considerably larger. From the centre to the circumference it measures nearly five cubits [194 cm, cf. p. 9], and in addition there is the surrounding square, which is also made of solid steel. The quadrant proper is covered, on the side where the divisions are, with a brass plate in such an ingenious way that one would think that it were soldered to the iron. The reason for this is that brass can stand fine divisions better than steel, however smooth, and, further, that it is not so apt to become rusty. The single degrees are divided not only into single minutes, but every minute is further subdivided into six small parts, so that the instrument indicates ten seconds of arc. The division is made according to the special method which we also use elsewhere. The square surrounding the quadrant is not covered with brass, because it is more seldom used, since the quadrant itself gives all that is required with sufficient accuracy. The square, however, even if it serves no other purpose, surrounds the quadrant for the sake of support and in order to make the turning of the instrument more convenient. Still, this too is furnished with divisions on the steel itself, and very fine divisions at that, also according to our special method. In this way the sides surrounding the circumference of the quadrant, both the horizontal DC, and the vertical BC, contain information corresponding to a five-figure sine-table, and the alidade, extending from the centre over the entire surface, when the observation is made indicates the required altitude on the quadrant as well as on the square, on the former by means of degrees of equal length, on the latter with the aid of the trigonometrical sine-calculation, the same result being obtained in both cases. By the quadrant we mean AGME, by the square ABCD, and by the alidade APQ, with a pinnule and diopters at P and, further, a cylinder at the centre A, just as in the case of the previous instruments. The part PQ of the alidade, which extends beyond the quadrant, can be produced to the extent that it reaches the corner of the square, farthest from the centre, or it can be shortened as may be desired. This instrument also has its supports and braces to make it steady and to keep it in position, not so many, however, as the previous instrument, since it is entirely of metal. Moreover their weight would otherwise be excessive, since these ribs (as one might call them), denoted by the letters GHNO and EKLM, and crossing each other, are made of solid steel, and hold the whole square, as well as the quadrant surrounded by it, rigidly in their plane and in the correct position. The quadrant and its square are fastened to a very strong iron pillar at XY, together with which it can be turned around conveniently and easily in any direction. This pillar turns above within a round hole in the middle of an iron grid denoted by the letters A [should be a] and solidly fixed across in the wall of the crypt. Below, it turns on an iron plate at Y in the same way as described for the previous instrument, so that the whole instrument can be adjusted for use with the aid of screws, set here in four different places, and so that while turning round it is kept rigidly in the proper plane. The plate mentioned is fixed with its screws to a round stone pillar, denoted by b, which also carries the whole instrument, while deep down in the ground it rests upon another stone foundation. This instrument is also provided with its azimuth horizon, TVW, on the circular wall of the crypt. The azimuth horizon is completely covered with brass and placed nearly half way up the wall, so that the observer, when standing on the uppermost step (for this instrument also has its steps, made of brick, upon which one can walk up and down as required by the observations, and on account of the size of the instrument these steps are necessary) can read the azimuths which are indicated by the pointers R and S on both sides. The diameter of this azimuth horizon is sufficiently great, to make it possible to walk within it and all around the whole quadrant with its square, this diameter being nine cubits [350 cm, cf. p. 9]. The instrument in itself is rigidly joined together and secured by screws so that, once the instrument is correctly set up, it is hardly to be feared that it should be moved out of position by human violence. So much for the construction and setting up of the instrument. On the upper part of the wall is a carefully constructed roof that protects the instrument against damage by weather. This roof also has its windows which can be opened, and it can be turned around as required by the observations on wheels that carry it. Furthermore, the windows can be shut while the instrument is adjusted, in order that the wind should not force its plumb-lines D out of their natural position. When the instrument is not used, they protect it against damage by rain and wind. And the roof and its details are arranged in the same way as with the previous quadrant, as explained there.

The use is similar to that of the previous instrument, when the object is to observe and note altitudes as well as azimuths, in so far as this is of importance to Astronomy, as indicated before. Since this quadrant, with its square, is entirely of metal, and also larger than the previous instrument, it indicates altitudes as well as azimuths with still higher accuracy, so that it is possible to determine these even within one-sixth of a minute. Such a high degree of accuracy is required, and well worth the trouble, when the motion of the sun is to be determined from its altitude and declination.

Finally I wish to add that these two quadrants, namely, the previous or the revolving one, and this steel quadrant, which is also revolving, are the instruments which we have chiefly depended upon, in addition to consulting the very large brass quadrant, the Mural or Tychonian one (on which see below [should be above, cf. p. 29]), when the problem was to find the declination of the sun, in order to determine, without error, its position and its entire orbit. We have used the same procedure in investigations of the declinations of the stars during their transit over the meridian, a matter requiring the greatest precision. When these three large instruments were properly adjusted and ready for use, they indicated the same altitude within an insignificant fraction of a minute of arc, agreeing in every respect. The sextants and other instruments when used together with them also gave evidence in their favour.

SEMICIRCULUS MAGNUS AZIMU-
THALIS

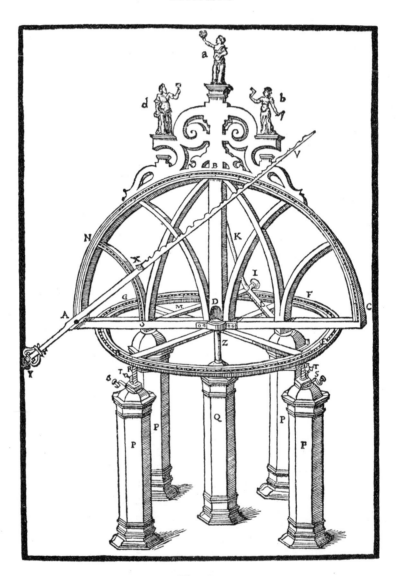

Fig. 8.

SEMICIRCULUS MAGNUS AZIMUTHALIS

GREAT AZIMUTH SEMICIRCLE

DESCRIPTION AND USE OF THE INSTRUMENT

We have also devised another instrument suitable for accurate measures of altitudes and azimuths, the appearance of which can be seen from the figure [Fig. 8]. Here I have preferred to make use of a whole semicircle ABC instead of a quadrant, yet placing the centre of the divisions at A on the diameter AC, since the length of the single degrees on the circumference of the semicircle in this way has twice the value it would have had with divisions made from its centre. For from Euclid's Elements it is known that an angle from the centre of the circle to its periphery is twice the angle from the periphery to the periphery itself, according to the twentieth chapter of the third book, and the other chapters that lead to the same result. In the middle of the semicircle a quadrilateral oblong tube extends from the centre D to the topmost point B. Inside this a plumb-line, the lead of which is visible together with a piece of the brass string in the hole D, indicates when the instrument is erected vertically so that it coincides with the plane of the vertical semicircle. The framework extending in both directions, on both sides in the form of arcs, is mounted only for support and for keeping the immense semicircle in its plane and with the correct circular shape. The diameter AC of the circle is six cubits [233 cm, cf. p. 9]. The length of the alidade YAV which is placed upon it, measured from A to V, is equal to the diameter of the semicircle. The alidade has, further, an extension AY which is somewhat thicker in order to facilitate the raising and lowering of the alidade, which is hereby balanced. For this reason also it is provided with two handles of solid metal at Y. On the other side is a spring with a screw at X, where it can be fastened to the small quadrant NO, in order that the alidade may be kept in the required position until the altitude has been read off, whatever its position relative to the rim of the semicircle. The semicircular instrument is also covered all over with brass plates, as far as this was necessary. On top it carries three figures cleverly and artfully carved out of strong wood. These are placed on bases, as appears from the figure, and their purpose is not only for ornament, but also that they should represent a symbolical meaning. For the figure that is placed highest is Urania representing Astronomy herself. She is a beautiful shapely virgin, turning her face towards the sky and contemplating the stars. With her right hand she is holding up the sphere of the celestial revolutions, while with her left hand she receives the objects extended towards her by the two women who stand lower, and who are to be imagined as being in her service. Her coat is sky-blue, woven with golden stars and covered with silver fringes. The woman, standing below and to the left of Urania, is a symbol of Geometry. In her right hand she has a triangle which she extends towards Astronomy, and in the other a pair of compasses. By this she indicates that she is serving Astronomy by measurement and by mechanical construction, and also by the learned science of Trigonometry. She is looking up in the direction of Urania's face, and looks at her with awe. The colour of her coat is somewhat brownish, woven with green, because she is named after that pertaining to the earth. On her head she wears a laurel wreath, thereby showing that she is eternal and able to grasp pure truth. The virgin standing on the other, or right, side represents Arithmetic. She too is looking up to Astronomy, showing awe and serving her. In one hand she is holding a piece of chalk, in the other a tablet, expressing hereby that she represents the numbers which Astronomy needs in order to be understood, and that she analyses into discrete quantities that which Geometry first proved by general mathematical relations. She too wears a laurel wreath, since she is as eternal and true as Geometry. The colour of her clothes is white, resembling paper or parchment, with various numbers inscribed on both sides. The meaning of all this is partly that it should decorate the instrument, partly that it should show that Astronomy is the highest of the liberal sciences and, as it were, their Queen, and that it has attached to itself as servants Geometry and Arithmetic in preference to all other sciences, although this does not mean that it looks down on the latter. Below this semicircle is an azimuth horizon EFIGH measuring four cubits [155 cm, cf. p. 9] in diameter. It is made of solid steel and on the surface suitably divided into degrees and their subdivisions. It is provided in the middle with two strong iron bars cutting each other crosswise at the centre D, around which the whole instrument turns. A few iron braces, which will keep the instrument at right angles to the fixed horizon, are mounted on the back. Below the iron horizon are five pillars. Of these the one in the middle, which is denoted by Q, is right under the centre, while the other four, denoted by P, carry the circumference, the four points of support being equidistant. Furthermore all four have on top a special kind of screw, the so-called endless screws. These are denoted by the letter R, which must be implied for the rest of them [i. e. those invisible in the figure]. With the aid of small handles ST, that can be turned to and fro, they can be pushed upward or downward until the azimuth circle, that rests upon them, is exactly parallel to the horizon, and the semicircle standing on the latter is brought into a vertical plane. For these screws can without difficulty raise or lower even a very great weight, and they may be very useful in other ways also, where mechanical tasks are concerned.

The use of the instrument is sufficiently clear from its construction. It is used in the same way as when deductions are normally made from azimuths and altitudes, with the sole difference that here one carries out and reads on a semicircle what would otherwise be obtained with quadrants or azimuth alidades, as we shall explain later on. I will make the following remark, however. The steel quadrant surrounded by a square, of which we have spoken in connection with the previous figure [Fig. 7], was at first so constructed that it rested with its lower part on a steel horizon, and was turned around upon it, as we have shown in another figure, which, however, is not reproduced here. Later we found it more practical to let it turn freed from this horizontal support, as is shown in the previous figure [Fig. 7], because it weighed far too heavily on the horizon, being as already mentioned entirely of steel, and thus could hardly be turned around without setting the whole instrument in motion or shaking it. Still, it is possible to arrange its construction in this way, and in that case no concave wall is needed around it to carry the azimuth circle, nor iron grids above and below, as with the previous instrument. Perhaps we shall some time give a figure showing this construction together with a description of it, although the procedure described before is much more convenient and surer. [Cf. Fig. 21, p. 92, and pp. 93—94, where this construction is shown and described.]

INSTRUMENTUM PARALLATICUM SIVE
REGULARUM

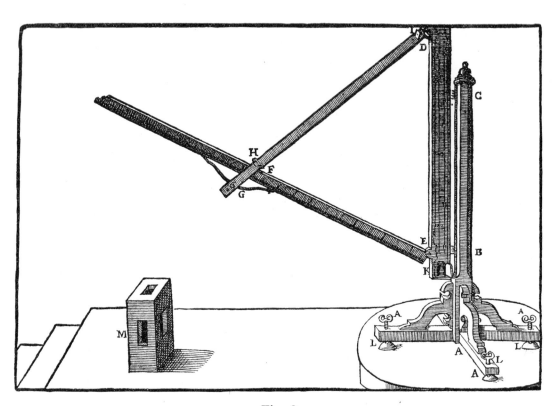

Fig. 9.

INSTRUMENTUM PARALLATICUM SIVE REGULARUM

THE PARALLATIC OR RULER-INSTRUMENT

DESCRIPTION AND USE OF THE INSTRUMENT

This parallatic instrument, which is also called the Ptolemaic rulers, I have wished to construct, since it requires very few accessories, namely, three rulers, in order to measure in a moment the zenith distance of a star, and hence its altitude. An instrument of this kind has come into my possession, made entirely of wood which previously belonged to the incomparable Copernicus, and was even, it was said, made by him with his own hand. It was sent to me as a gift from Master Johannes Hannow, a canon from Ermeland, where Copernicus used to live, and where in the year 1584 I had sent one of my collaborators who helped me in the astronomical work [Elias Olsen] with a sextant of the same kind as that described by me in the third chapter [cf. p. 25]. My intention was that he should measure, with the help of this instrument, as accurately as possible, the altitude of the pole in Ermeland [at Frauenburg]. For I supposed that the value of this quantity determined by Copernicus was nearly three minutes too small. My attention had been drawn to this by the discrepancy between the actual orbit of the sun and the obliquity of the ecliptic on the one hand, and Copernicus' values on the other. That such was the case was confirmed by observation. With my instrument it was found from a great number of observations of fixed stars as well as of the sun that the altitude of the pole for that place was 54°22$^{1}/_{4}$′, as has been demonstrated in more detail by us in the first volume of the *Progymnasmata astronomica*, p. 34 f. [Opera Omnia II, p. 30] where I point out the reason for the error which Copernicus made in determining incorrectly the course of the sun. Copernicus assumed that the latitude of the place in question according to his observations was 54°19$^{1}/_{2}$′, which is 2$^{3}/_{4}$′ smaller than the accurate value. This is in agreement with the conclusion I had previously drawn from his data and from the deduced numerical solution for the course of the sun. When my collaborator came back to me, he brought with him not only the sextant with which I had provided him, completely undamaged, but also this other parallatic instrument of Copernicus', as a gift from the canon mentioned. The moment I saw it, although it was wooden and inconvenient to use, I was so delighted, because it reminded me of the great master who was said to have constructed it, that I could not help writing, immediately, a heroic poem, which is to be found in the first volume of the astronomical letters p. 295 f. [should be 235, Opera Omnia VI, p. 266 f.]. Shortly afterwards I had another similar instrument made, covered with brass plates. Hereby I introduced a few minor changes and additions in order to make it more convenient to use, and it is this modified instrument that is shown here [Fig. 9]. There are three rulers, DE, EF, and FD. The first of these, ED, which points towards the zenith is connected above at D with another that can revolve in a round brass groove. They are equal in length, each of them being four cubits [155 cm, cf. p. 9], counting the length of the upper one from the letter D to F. The protruding section FG has been added solely for the purpose of surrounding and holding the other, flatter ruler, the former being split. The third ruler, EH, however, which is longer and connected with DE, the first, in the same way at E, where it can be turned, has the length required in order that the two sides DE and EF [should be DF] can form a right angle, the ruler DF being in this case lifted so as to be parallel to the horizon. The diopters, through which one points to the stars, are on the same ruler at H and I and accomplish the purpose by observations through slits, which above and below are parallel to the preceding pinnule, in the way invented by us. The Copernican instrument instead of these had holes, through which it is very difficult to observe the stars. There is the further disadvantage that the forward hole, that in the pinnule I, has to be larger than the second one, for convenience in observing the stars through it, and in that case it must necessarily cover a certain, not very small, fraction of a degree, namely, at least one-eighth or one-tenth. During the observation one does not know, whether the star is exactly at the centre of the hole or not, and thus an inaccuracy of a few minutes of arc may be introduced, so that one wonders how not only Copernicus, but also the ancients, who made use of diopters of this kind, were able to obtain anything certain in this way, even if the rest had been correctly constructed. Equidistant divisions are marked on the flatter ruler with the aid of transversal points according to our usual procedure. There are so many of them that they reach the last six-figure number of the sine-table [i. e. unity] at the correct point, namely the point indicating the same length as that of the two first rulers, so that an equilateral triangle is formed. Further it should be mentioned that the ruler DK, which points towards the zenith, has a cavity inside, in which a thin brass string, hanging down from above, carries a plumb weight at its lower end near K. This is in order that the string carrying the weight inside should not be set in motion by the wind. A few oblong openings are placed on this cavity, and these can be opened and shut as may be required for the purpose. The string, with the aid of a suitable marking which is placed there indicates when the side DE points exactly to the zenith. This can be effected with the help of screws below on the base at A, which turn on pieces of iron at L. For the three rulers are hung on a pillar CB standing on the base mentioned, in such a way that they can be turned to and fro on round pivots. This practical arrangement, with the support, I added to this instrument. It did not exist on the Copernican instrument. I also added a small spring at G which has the effect that the ruler AF [should be DF] stays at any observed angle, until the reading on the side of the longer ruler has been carried out. I also made a few other additions to make the instrument more convenient to use. These, however, I shall not explain in detail in order not to create the impression that I underrated the inventions of my predecessors by correcting them too much.

The use of this parallatic instrument is for observations of the zenith distances of the stars, in the way Ptolemy used to do it with the moon, particularly to find its maximum latitude, although he did not succeed in determining this with sufficient accuracy and generality, as is apparent from the determination of the lunar orbit which we have carried out in a supplement to the first chapter of the volume of the *Progymnasmata* already mentioned [Opera Omnia II, p. 121 f.]. Here it is shown with the aid of accurate observations that the maximum latitude of the moon at the time of full moon is different from that at the quadratures. The difference is quite clear and may amount to one-third of a degree, as is developed in more detail in the place quoted, with indications of the particular relations and circumstances. The angular distance FDE from the zenith can be found with the aid of the table of tangents or the sine-table, use being made of the divisions on the line FE. For in the triangle two sides of equal length FD and ED are given, while the third is read on the longest ruler, when the observation has been made. Hence the angle FDE measuring the zenith distance of the star, the complement of which is the required altitude, can be found. These rulers also have the advantage that it is easy to separate them from each other and pack them and transport them to any desired place. In actual practice they do not yield results with the accuracy and certainty of the quadrants described before, however carefully they be constructed. For it is very difficult for the rulers to keep perfectly straight. If they are too long they bend by their own weight so that they will deviate from a straight line, and if they are too short they will not yield what is expected of them on account of their limited size.

PARALLATICUM ALIUD SIVE REGULÆ
TAM ALTITUDINES QUAM AZIMUTHA
EXPEDIENTES

Fig. 10.

PARALLATICUM ALIUD SIVE REGULÆ TAM ALTITUDINES QUAM AZIMUTHA EXPEDIENTES

ANOTHER PARALLATIC OR RULER-INSTRUMENT WHICH SHOWS THE ALTITUDES AS WELL AS THE AZIMUTHS

DESCRIPTION AND USE OF THE INSTRUMENT

A few years before I had built up some other rulers inside a tower which, when they were turned around as desired, filled it entirely. In doing so I followed a particular method, which was partly an imitation of the ancient principle due to Hipparchus (if tradition is trustworthy). But, besides, they were provided with certain novel additions, which I had invented with the purpose of making them more stable and convenient to use. Their construction is apparent from the accompanying figure [Fig. 10]. Here AD represents the first and fundamental ruler, which is placed horizontally and can be turned around, when this is necessary. Its length is $8^1/_2$ cubits [330 cm, cf. p. 9], and on its upper surface it carries the numbers corresponding to a five-figure sine-table, ingeniously divided according to my habit by transversal points, twice numbered. The combined length of the two other rulers are equal to the length of the ruler just considered when they are lowered onto the latter. They are denoted by AB and BC, and measure $4^1/_4$ cubits each [165 cm, cf. p. 9]. The first one, AB, is fastened to the beginning of the long one at A, so that it can be raised and lowered and at the same time draw with it the second one, or BC, which is joined to it by a hinge at B. On these two smaller rulers there are no divisions. Only the foremost one, AB, has diopters and pinnules, through which one points using slits in the lower pinnule at E, where the eye is placed. The rims of the upper pinnule at F are completely parallel to the former. Thus it is possible to sight through these in any direction, when altitudes are concerned as well as when the question is of azimuths. All these three rulers are entirely of brass, very finely smoothed and polished, and they are of quadrangular form and of suitable thickness in order not to be bent. In order to facilitate the raising and lowering of the two upper rulers, an upright stand denoted by LNOP is mounted and supported by braces below, denoted by PVZ.

At V is a screw which through the circular disc W guides the braces to and fro on the base that is built under the whole instrument (see below), in order that it should not be weighed down by its own weight. The vertical stand has the function that, as already mentioned, it can raise and lower the upper rulers, as desired, and further keep them within their plane, so that they are not drawn towards either side. They are raised and lowered with the aid of a rope KLNM, which can be pulled conveniently over a small wheel on top at LN, and this rope is fastened to the front ruler at K, where a piece of metal, placed below and able to revolve on a round pivot, has an aperture that is sufficiently large to allow the pinnule at F to be distinguished by an eye at the diopter E without any obstruction in between. A further convenience is that the position of the instrument can be examined with the aid of a plumb-line ending at Q, viz. to see whether AD is exactly horizontal, since LNPO is at right angles to it. As a matter of fact, this can also be ascertained with the aid of the plumb-line BR, for this must in all cases intersect the line AC at the mid point between A and C. Two quadrants IGH completely covered with brass plates hold the front ruler by means of a stiff spring at H, so that it moves between them, thus facilitating the desired raising and keeping in position of the rulers and preventing any motion sideways, so that in all positions they are in the same plane as the longer lower part, no matter how they are raised and lowered. From the centre A to the circumference I the quadrants measure about three cubits [117 cm, cf. p. 9]. Finally the point where the divisions are to be read, when the observation has been made,, for instance at C, is exactly indicated with the aid of a steel pointer. On both sides of C there are steel springs which also serve the purpose of keeping the ruler BC in position, so that it will not be bent down by its own weight.

Further XW indicates the base (that I have spoken of before) upon which the whole instrument rests on one side, particularly the back part of it, and around which it turns. On top of this base is an endless screw at T similar to those I have mentioned before in connection with the semicircular instrument [cf. p. 42]. When this is raised or lowered with the aid of the handle at T, it guides the whole instrument in the correct way, so that the lower, or longest ruler is exactly horizontal. Finally the outer end of the ruler D also rests on a circular wall, denoted by the letters Y, and below it on the same solid wall is an azimuth circle of brass, suitably divided and parallel to the plane of the horizon, and at level with the base mentioned. The diameter of the circle is twelve cubits [466 cm, cf. p. 9].

The use of the instrument depends on the fact that it will indicate the altitudes (with the aid of the rulers proper, at the point of contact with the lower one) as well as the azimuths, at the place, where the edge of this ruler with the pointer at D touches the azimuth horizon and indicates a certain point. With regard to the altitudes it is seen that the two sides represented by the rulers AB and BC are equal, while the third side AC is determined by the observation and the reading. Hence the angle BAC that indicates the required altitude is known. The same end can also be obtained in another way, namely, by reading the point of the division, where the plumb-line BR touches the lower ruler, counting the distance from A. In that case a right-angled triangle is given, one side of which is known according to the construction of the instrument, while the length of the other is read after the observation. Hence the required angle at A is known. What purposes the altitudes and azimuths serve is taught in pragmatic Astronomy, as previously elaborated by us.

This instrument, which surpasses the previous ruler-instrument in size and length, shows everything with greater accuracy and is more stable and easier to use, particularly for the determination of altitudes. When the problem is to determine azimuths as well, there are certain difficulties, precisely on account of the great size and weight of the instrument. This difficulty may be overcome, however, if care be taken to set the lower ruler, before the observation, to some azimuth towards which the star to be observed is moving, and then before the altitude is taken, with the aid of the plumb-lines, to check that the adjustment of the instrument is correct in every respect, both horizontally and vertically. Then it will be possible to determine both the altitude and the azimuth without sensible error, as well with this instrument as with the largest quadrants described above.

———

ARMILLÆ ZODIACALES

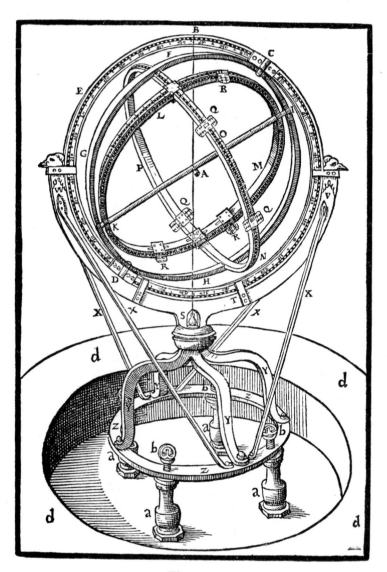

Fig. 11.

ARMILLÆ ZODIACALES
ZODIACAL ARMILLARY INSTRUMENT
DESCRIPTION AND USE OF THE INSTRUMENT

The instruments hitherto described are particularly intended for observations of altitudes and azimuths, either separately or together. Since, however, the use of these instruments for astronomical purposes essentially requires trigonometrical calculations which are not easily comprehensible to everybody and particularly cumbersome to certain people who shun labour, certain other appliances have been invented, with the aid of which the latitudes and longitudes of the stars, the two quantities particularly required, can be found with little inconvenience and without troublesome calculations. I find that two of these in particular were used by the ancients. One is the so-called armillary instrument that was used by Hipparchus and Ptolemy, who gave it its name. The other is called the torquetum, an instrument which in my opinion was invented by the Arabians or the Chaldæans, and used by them. With its circular plane surfaces it serves the same purposes as the former with its armillae. I have not yet wished to construct the torquetum, because, if it is to have the required size, it will be oppressed by its own weight and be difficult to handle. Should anybody wish to know how it is constructed, however, he can look it up in the Opus Astronomicum Cæsareum of Appianus, towards the end, or in Schoner's little book on the same subject, before the observations of the famous Regiomontanus and those of his pupil, Walther of Nürnberg, and there he will find what he wants. An armillary instrument was previously made by me, in which, however, I changed the construction of Hipparchus and Ptolemy somewhat, in order to obtain greater convenience in use. A delineation of the instrument is seen in the figure [Fig. 11]. This instrument consists of four armillae [rings] only (while my predecessors used five or six). Of these the first one, EBCNH, represents the meridian, and this armilla must be placed in such a way that it coincides with the celestial meridian. On it are the poles of the equator, C and D, which can be raised or lowered until they correspond exactly with the latitude of the place where the observation is made. This is checked by means of the plumb-line BS that is fastened above at the zenith, where

8

the division of the meridian shows the complement of the altitude of the pole. Below it is at the same distance from the other pole. This meridian confines all the other armillae, the first of these being GFIH which at right angles to its plane carries the second zodiacal armilla POQN with its poles at IK, at an angular distance from the equinoctial poles mentioned above equal to the distance between the poles of the ecliptic and the equator, viz. the maximum declination of the zodiac. This quantity we have several times found to be, at present, exactly equal to $23°31^1/_2'$, slightly different from the determination of our predecessors. A round brass tube IAK passes through the poles of this zodiac. At its centre A the tube carries a cylinder, this being a practical addition to the instrument used by the ancients. Around the poles of the zodiac, and inside the latter, turns another armilla, denoted by KLRM, which serves for the determination of the latitude. Further the zodiacal armilla itself carries four pinnules which according to our custom are provided with slits. Of these three are seen at the letters Q while the fourth is invisible. The latitude armilla also carries four pinnules of the same kind at R. Here, too, the fourth one is hidden. All pinnules are of brass. The armillae, too, are all covered with brass and on their outer sides carry divisions with our usual transversal points. The meridian is of massive steel in order to be able to carry securely the inner armillae. Its diameter is three cubits [117 cm, cf. p. 9]. From this the diameter of the inner ones that are adjacent to it, can be inferred. Furthermore these armillae have a base, worked in strong, solid iron, upon which their whole weight rests. It is denoted by the letters VTDWYZ. There is a hole in the base at S for the lead of the plumb-line. The lower part of the base, the iron ring b, is pierced at four equidistant points by screws resting on four stone pillars provided with small iron discs at a. With the aid of the screws the whole instrument can be raised or lowered in such a way that all its armillae with regard to their planes and directions correspond exactly to the celestial circles which they represent. Four iron braces X are added to make sure that the base and with it the whole instrument will not shift on account of its weight towards one side or the other. Further a few steps d are added, upon which one can stand if necessary when observations are made or readings taken. This instrument also requires a special little tower, the roof of which is constructed in such a way that one half of it may be removed while the other half may be turned around if desired.

The use of these, as well as the other Ptolemaic armillae, is for measuring the longitudes and latitudes of the stars. Two observers are required for these observations. One of them sets any of the pinnules on the zodiacal armilla to the point corresponding to the longitude of some known fixed star. He then sights the same fixed star through both slits, and on both sides along the axis IK, and at the same time keeps all armillae fixed in such a way that the plane of the ecliptic-armilla coincides exactly with the celestial ecliptic. In the meantime the other observer moves any of the other pinnules on the zodiac until it fits best for the star, the longitude of which he is trying to determine. When this is the case he will see the star equally well through both slits along the axis mentioned. Then this pinnule will indicate the required longitude on the zodiacal armilla. In order, further, to find the latitude one has to set the latitude-armilla to the same longitude with regard to the ecliptic as that found for the star, and then move one of its pinnules up or down until this star is seen through both slits along the cylinder A, above as well as below. The pinnule will then indicate the required latitude, which is to be read on the latitude-armilla mentioned, up or down from the ecliptic, according as the latitude is south or north. In this fashion the longitude as well as the latitude of the star, whose position one had resolved to find, will easily be determined. Although this armillary instrument is suitable for determining quickly and easily the positions of the stars, and in the form described, as constructed by us, is less apt than others to let the armillae of which it consists move out of their correct plane, yet it cannot guarantee that no error of one minute of arc, or two, is introduced, particularly since the zodiacal armilla does not everywhere turn round in the position of equilibrium, and hence on account of its weight is moved, and also moves the others a little out of their correct planes, and even in different ways. Consequently we did not use this kind of armillary instrument very often, and particularly not when the greatest precision was required. We have preferred to invent other equatorial armillae which are free from this error, an error which it is impossible to remove by the use of larger zodiacal armillae, since the weight of the armillae then becomes that much greater. If smaller ones are used, the error is less noticeable, but on account of their smaller sizes they do not allow observations of a precision of one minute of arc.

ARMILLÆ ÆQUATORIÆ

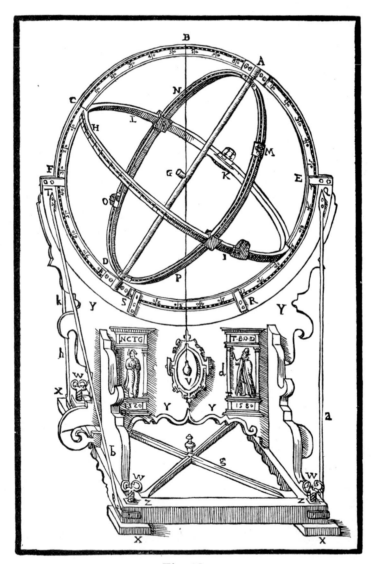

Fig. 12.

ARMILLÆ ÆQUATORIÆ

EQUATORIAL ARMILLARY INSTRUMENT

DESCRIPTION AND USE OF THE INSTRUMENT

We have also invented some equatorial armillae which, having been adjusted on both sides in conformity with the axis of the celestial poles, will not be drawn towards one side or the other by their weight, nor have their planes forced out of coincidence with those of the circles which they represent. This is what was wanting in the previous instrument for the reasons mentioned. The form of the instrument can be seen from the accompanying figure [Fig. 12]. There are but three armillae [rings] with a round axis. They measure the right ascensions of the stars as well as their declinations. The first one, AESF, which is the largest, surrounds and carries the others. It represents the meridian. Its diameter is about four cubits [155 cm, cf. p. 9]. From this the size of the others within can be inferred. The latter armillae are adjusted and regulated according to the plane of the former. Through A and the point opposite, D, there is, as mentioned, a round axis, which can revolve together with the inner armilla and serves for the measurements of declination. In the middle, at a point which is also the centre of all the armillae, it carries at G a cylinder which is fixed at right angles to the axis and has a diameter equal to that of the axis itself. The axis can be raised together with the meridian, through which it extends along a diameter, until the plumb-line BV passes points, above and below, on the division which indicates single minutes of arc, that correspond to the complement of the altitude of the pole of the place in question, and until, further, the plumb-line shows the same distance from the place of the meridian above and below, or else lightly touches it in both places. The inner armilla which, as I have said, indicates the declinations, is denoted by NMPO. Sometimes it may coincide with the plane of the meridian, and within it the armilla may be turned in any direction according to the requirements corresponding to the position of the star to be observed. In the two places where it surrounds and meets the other armilla, which is at right angles to it and corresponds to the equator, it carries on the outside a plate indicating the degrees and minutes of the equator, on one side as well as on the opposite. Furthermore it carries its pinnules at four places, namely, in the quadrants. Only two of these are shown here, at M and O. They contain parallel slits having a mutual distance equal to the diameter of the cylinder at G and the thickness of the axis AD. Each quadrant on the outer side of the armilla, viz. the side closest to the eye, is divided into 90 degrees, and each of these into 60 minutes with the aid of transversal points according to the method which we generally employ and have described several times. The other armilla which is at right angles to this, and which, as I said, corresponds to the equator, is denoted by HLKI. In two places, at C and at the diametrically opposite point, it is joined to the meridian already mentioned, and it is exactly at right angles to it, resting immovable in it. On the outer side it is also finely divided into all the degrees of the circle and their minutes. It carries four pinnules, shaped in the same way as those in the previous armilla. Two of these are shown here, at IK on one half of the circle, while one has to imagine the two others similarly on the other half. All pinnules are ingeniously worked in brass, but the meridian proper is entirely of massive steel in order to be able to carry the other armillae within it. The two armillae crossing each other at right angles within the first one, are, as I have mentioned, covered, though only on their outsides, with strong brass plates, which carry the divisions. They are not entirely covered with brass, because that would make them too heavy. They are made of pieces of wood joined together and bent into a circle, and many times coated with pitch, and in such an ingenious way that they are not formed of one solid piece of wood, but of several that are finely smoothed and flat, and very carefully glued together. The grain of each successive piece is reversed so that the directions of their respective tips and roots alternate. Experience has taught me that this is the way to treat wood intended for use in instruments in order to prevent bending and other changes. Of all kinds of wood walnut and the kind of spruce which the Germans call Feuchtenholtz are the best ones, provided they have not been damaged, and have been dried for a long time. When the armillae have been made in this way by glueing small wooden sticks together, and when they have got their proper shape and size, then fine linen or parchment is glued all round them, and they are coated and coloured with a mixture of white lead and linseed oil in order not to be too sensitive to changes of the weather. These armillae are carried by a base, which is also made of particularly solid and strong wood, shaped as appears in the figure where it is denoted by the letters Y. The quadrangular underframe, however, which is seen below, is provided with screws at its four corners, at X. With the aid of these the whole instrument is controlled so that it can be adjusted in conformity with the celestial circles which it represents. Four iron braces are added here, joined with the top of the base where it touches [i. e. carries] the meridian. They support and strengthen the instrument in order that the armillae shall not shift towards one side or the other. The first is denoted by FbX, the second by EaX, while the two others are behind the instrument. At the point where this base touches the meridian it is rounded to form a semicircle, in order that the meridian, which it carries, may have a complete and solid support. For this reason four metal clips are mounted at FSRE so that they grip the meridian in such a way that it can be turned around slowly and cautiously, until its axis corresponds to the celestial polar axis, and is thus kept in position without moving. Below, on the sides of this base, and on both sides of the opening containing the lead weight at V, are four beautifully painted pictures for the sake of ornament. These represent Ptolemy, Al Battani, Copernicus, and myself. Two of these portraits, namely, those of Copernicus and myself, are seen at d, while the two others are hidden behind. The construction of the rest of this base, including the cross-bars at g and other pieces for support or decoration, will be sufficiently clear from the figure, if it be carefully examined.

The use of the instrument is, as already mentioned, for observations of the declinations and the right ascensions of the stars. For when the armilla DNMP is turned about its axis towards the star to be observed, then its pinnules are turned up and down along it, until the star, whichever it may be, is sighted along the cylinder G, equally bright above and below it. Then the pinnule indicates the required declination on the divisions on the outer brass plate. On the other armilla which is at right angles to the one first considered, a suitable pinnule is directed towards a star, the right ascension of which has been determined beforehand in one way or another. That one of the other pinnules which is best suited for the purpose is, by another observer (for in this case there must be two) directed towards the other star, until this, too, is seen along both sides of the axis of the instrument. Next the arc between the two pinnules is read, and this indicates the difference between the right ascensions of the stars. When this quantity is added to, or subtracted from, the known right ascension, as required by the relative positions, then the previously unknown right ascension is obtained. The same result can be achieved if the declination-armilla is set to the position corresponding to the known right ascension, and the known star is observed along this, while one of the pinnules on the equatorial armilla is moved by another observer, until the star, the right ascension of which is to be determined, is seen on both sides of the axis. Then the same pinnule will indicate, on the outer rim of the equator, the required angle, without the necessity of an addition or a subtraction. The importance of exact determinations of right ascensions and declinations of stars, and also the method by which their longitudes and latitudes can easily be derived from these, are well known to all trained in Astronomy, and we shall, God willing, briefly explain these matters elsewhere.

ARMILLÆ ALIÆ ÆQUATORIÆ

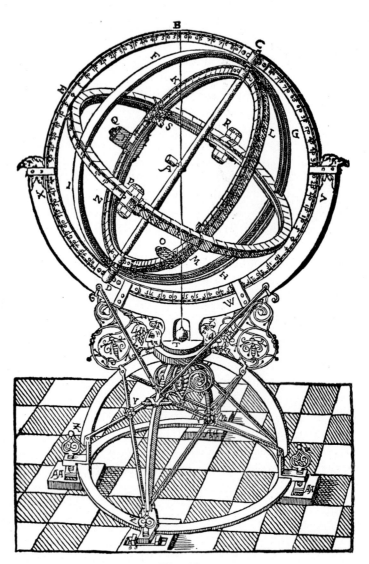

Fig. 13.

ARMILLÆ ALIÆ ÆQUATORIÆ
ANOTHER EQUATORIAL ARMILLARY INSTRUMENT
DESCRIPTION AND USE OF THE INSTRUMENT

I have also had another armillary instrument of the same size made, which is seen in the figure [Fig. 13]. As before the outer armilla [ring] represents the meridian. It is entirely of steel, carefully smoothed all over and provided with divisions extending over the whole of the circle, so that it also contains the single minutes. With this instrument one has to imagine all the rest, as far as the plumb-line, the poles and the axis are concerned, similar to the previous armillary instrument. The number of armillae within the first one is three, so that the whole instrument consists of four armillae, or one more than the previous instrument. In addition there is a round axis and a cylinder fixed to it. They may easily serve the same purpose as an armilla. The reason why this instrument has three inner armillae besides the meridian is that the equator is movable instead of fixed as in the case of the previous instrument. Therefore it needs the armilla IFGH which supports and surrounds it, and is at right angles to it. This armilla, too, is made of pure steel in order to strengthen it for its task, but it is not provided with any divisions. The equator, however, which I have mentioned, and which is denoted by PSR, is provided with divisions to single minutes, and they are even found on both surfaces, as is necessary when they are to be used for determinations of right ascensions as well as for indicating moments of time. On it are mounted pinnules at R and P, and a few others in addition, which are not shown here, for use in the observations. They are constructed as in the previous instrument, and the division, too, is made in the same way. Another armilla nearer the centre, denoted by the letters NKLM, as before serves the purpose of finding the declinations. It can be turned around within the equatorial armilla, which it cuts at right angles, so that it also indicates, at the place where it touches it, points of the equator with the aid of small plates at S and M, fitting on to it. Furthermore it carries its pinnules at Q and O, and two more, which are not shown here, but which must be imagined similarly on the other side. There are also divisions on it, corresponding to the various quadrants, minute by minute. All these armillae, surrounded by the meridian, are entirely covered with brass plates, and this has been done so finely and smoothly that one would think that they were cast entirely from solid brass. The round axis, too, is of brass, as are the pinnules. The plumb-line BT is made of a thin brass wire, as is also our custom in other cases. Any detail that may have been passed over here may be inferred from the figure, as for the previous instrument. This armillary instrument rests on a support, or base, of solid steel, denoted by XTVYZ and the other intervening letters. The upper semi-circular part of it, XDWV, holds all along its length the lower part of the meridian proper, which itself surrounds, and so carries, the other armillae. As with the previous instrument four clips are mounted on it. The further elaboration of this base is clearly seen from the figure. Other parts have been added for decoration besides those for use and reinforcement, and these also help to strengthen the instrument which, as already stated, is wholly of solid steel. At the bottom is a thick iron ring Z, which serves to support the whole instrument. At four equidistant points screws are mounted on it. Below these screws are placed some small iron discs on a quadrangular stone. The screws, when turned on the discs, adjust the whole instrument so that the armillae represent exactly their corresponding celestial circles. The adjustment is made by means of the plumb-line BT, which also ensures coincidence of the meridian plane of the instrument and the celestial meridian, besides giving the meridian its correct position with regard to the altitude of the pole. It even makes all the inner armillae conform to the celestial circles which they represent. The instrument in itself is quite solid, and does not easily suffer change, being entirely of metal.

The u s e of this instrument is similar to that of the previous one, only it is possible here to turn the equator at will inside the meridian circle. The declinations should be found, as before, on the declination armilla with the help of its cylinder placed at the centre A, use being made of suitable pinnules. The equatorial distances, or right ascensions, should be read, as before, on the equatorial armilla, which is at right angles to the one just mentioned, only in the case of this investigation the steel armilla carrying these may also be of some use. There is the additional advantage that when the right ascension of a star is determined in this way the point on the equator that is crossing the meridian indicates the right ascension of the zenith, and hence also the exact time, provided the position of the sun be exactly known, and the latter can be found in our tables. Another method is to set a fixed point in the equator to the meridian, and then by moving a pinnule along the former to find the distance of an arbitrary star along the equator, thus determining the time, as with the previous instrument, a matter which I neglected to indicate in connection with the latter. Thus it is easy, by means of these two armillary instruments, to determine in the sky both declinations and right ascensions as well as the exact time, all of which are extremely important in Astronomy. Anybody who might wish to inform himself in greater detail on the subject of the construction and use of this instrument can look it up in the first volume of our *Progymnasmata astronomica*, chapter II, pp. 250—252, at the bottom of the page [Opera Omnia II, pp. 250—253]. However, most of it, and the most important part, is sufficiently described here, in addition to a few other things.

I wish to add, however, that these armillae may be taken apart, and put together again, with the aid of certain screws. The same applies to the steel base, or support, so that the instrument can easily be moved to other places. This ought to be the case with all instruments, as far as possible, without damaging them. For an astronomer ought to be a citizen of the world, so that, if necessary or useful for him, he can move freely and at will to any other place and take his instruments with him, and not be confined to any one country. Since a very limited number of people occupy themselves with these celestial sciences and enterprises, and since it is very seldom that among the statesmen who wish to govern a state there are any so strongly attracted by these sciences that they consider it their duty to favour and support them, but are much more often repulsed by them and consider them futile, owing to their ignorance; so the person who cultivates divine Astronomy ought not to let himself be influenced by such ignorant judgments, but rather look down upon them from his elevated position, considering the cultivation of his studies the most precious of all things, and remaining indifferent to the coarseness of others. And when statesmen or others worry him too much, then he should leave with his possessions. For it is not even right to prefer one's native land, which attracts all mankind by her grace, and does not allow one to forget her, to these high celestial efforts bearing the stamp of immortality. But with a firm and steadfast mind one should hold, under all vicissitudes, that *everywhere the earth is below, and the sky above, and to the energetic man any region is his fatherland.*

ARMILLÆ AEQUATORIÆ MAXIMÆ
SESQUIALTERO CONSTANTES CIRCULO

Fig. 14.

ARMILLÆ AEQUATORIÆ MAXIMÆ SESQUIALTERO CONSTANTES CIRCULO

THE GREAT EQUATORIAL ARMILLARY INSTRUMENT WITH ONE COMPLETE CIRCLE, AND ONE SEMICIRCLE

DESCRIPTION AND USE OF THE INSTRUMENT

Although the two equatorial armillary instruments already delineated and described, and which were very costly, serve the purpose I have mentioned with sufficient accuracy I nevertheless later on invented and had constructed another one which need not be equipped with so many separate pieces. It has one complete armilla [ring] only which can revolve, and another semicircular one, which is fixed. With the aid of these two armillae all that I have said about the previous instruments can be carried out, in fact much more conveniently and without the difficulty involved in the previous instruments when the sighting has to be done near the equatorial armilla proper. For in that case the front part of it will obstruct the light, and it is also difficult to sight with the declination armilla in the neighbourhood of the equator, not to speak of various other drawbacks. This new armillary instrument has the further advantage that it can be constructed to a much larger size, as a consequence of which the degrees with their subdivisions can be reproduced more accurately, and yet owing to its stability and the way in which it is turned, it is practical and easier to use than the previous instruments. The construction of these large and particularly advantageous armillae is shown in the figure [Fig. 14], in so far as it is possible to reproduce them on a plane surface. The letters A denote the largest armilla, which is completely covered with brass plates. Its diameter is seven cubits [272 cm, cf. p. 9], and consequently the degrees are so large that every single minute is subdivided into four parts. The axis B of this armilla is of steel and quite round, but hollow inside in order to reduce the effects of its weight. Its diameter is three inches [cf. p. 9], and in the middle it carries a round brass cylinder, on both sides of which two brass alidades EF can turn close to the axis. These alidades carry pinnules at F close to the rim of the armilla, the diopters of which are provided with slits parallel to the cylinder.

Within the armilla one sees cross-bars, or braces, keeping the whole armilla rigidly together and supporting it to prevent deviations from its circular and plane form on account of its size. Below at D the axis ends in a rounded point sticking into a quadrangular steel disc provided with a corresponding pointed, narrowed hole. With the aid of screws mounted on both sides this can be moved a little in any desired direction. Upon it rests the round axis which keeps the whole armilla together, and also turns it round. The piece of iron below the steel disc is fixed to a big stone pillar, four cubits [155 cm, cf. p. 9] long, two cubits of which are below ground and rest on a solid foundation, while two cubits are visible and carry, on the front side, a statuette I representing Atlas, king of Mauretania, ingeniously chiselled in the same stone. His crown touches a stone globe, H, mounted on top of the pillar for the sake of decoration. The upper part of the axis rests on another iron bearing at C which lower down divides into two parts at K, ending in two branches, each securely fastened to a big and round solid stone pillar. These two pillars are sufficiently far apart to have a door between them through which one enters the instrument room. They are denoted by M and L. Above at C is a screw, which can move the piece of iron supporting the axis laterally so that the axis may be brought into the plane of the meridian. It is also possible to raise the axis in another way, both here and below at D, and move it cautiously until it coincides with the axis through the celestial poles. In this position it is then fixed. The other, semicircular, armilla is denoted by the letters O. It is carried by eight small stone pillars, denoted by P, so that it is kept rigidly in the plane of the equator. The same number of iron clips are mounted at points Q, and these keep and control the armilla in such a way that it accurately describes a semicircle, the centre of which is in the axis, and, further, so that it is in the plane of the equator without any deviation. It is all covered with brass, and the diameter is nine cubits [350 cm, cf. p. 9], with the result that it allows of the smallest subdivisions, even more so than the armilla proper. The purpose of making the semicircular armilla two cubits larger than the complete armilla is to make it possible to pass between the two if that is necessary. By way of a flight of stone-steps N (not shown here) one ascends and descends along the armilla, so that the eye of the observer can be conveniently placed close to it. There is another flight of round steps inside denoted by the letters T. This is used for ascending and descending all the way round, when observing with the complete armilla, as required by the higher or lower position of the star to be observed. At the two letters N one sees a wall, which surrounds the whole instrument and forms a sort of small turret or semisubterranean crypt around the whole instrument. Above is a roof which can be opened towards any desired direction, when observations are to be made, and afterwards closed in order that the precious instrument may be protected against damage from wind or rain.

The use of the instrument is for finding declinations with the aid of the circular revolving armilla by moving the diopters at F and pointing towards a star on both sides along the cylinder at E. Thus the required declination can be read at E [should be F]. This is possible in two ways, namely, by means of both diopters, the armilla being revolved so that the other side is now towards the eye. In this way the declination of one and the same star is determined twice. The two values found should agree with each other. On the other, semicircular armilla the pinnules at R are moved until the star to be observed is seen through the slits of the pinnule on both sides along the axis B. Then the pinnule itself shows on the semicircular armilla the equatorial distance from the meridian, either to the east or to the west. From this the time may be derived with the greatest accuracy from the known positions of the star and the sun. If, however, the right ascension of some star is required, then one observer directs one of the pinnules towards a star of known right ascension, while another observer similarly directs the other pinnule towards the star whose right ascension has to be determined in such a way that both stars at the same moment are seen along the same axis through the slits of the pinnules. For in that case the arc between the two pinnules will indicate the difference between their right ascensions. The required right ascension is then found as previously explained. Anybody wishing to learn more about the construction and use of this very large instrument, may consult the first volume of our Astronomical Letters p. 246 and the two following pages [Opera Omnia VI, p. 276—278], where various matters are described in greater detail, which have been left out here for the sake of brevity. Moreover the construction and use of the instrument is understood by careful study of the accompanying figure quicker than through an elaborate verbal explanation.

ARCUS BIPARTITUS MINORIBUS
SIDERUM DISTANTIIS INSERVIENS

Fig. 15.

ARCUS BIPARTITUS MINORIBUS SIDERUM DISTANTIIS INSERVIENS

THE BIPARTITE ARC FOR MEASURING SMALL ANGULAR DISTANCES OF STARS

DESCRIPTION AND USE OF THE INSTRUMENT

We have now spoken about the astronomical instruments which are used in various ways to investigate the altitudes and azimuths of the stars, and, further, those by which their longitudes and latitudes are ascertained, and in addition their declinations and right ascensions. It remains to deal with those for investigating their angular distances, and after that we shall speak of several others indiscriminately. With regard to the distances certain people in later years have constructed an astronomical radius which in itself is fairly manageable and easy to transport, and which moreover in theory is quite suitable for mathematical demonstration. In actual practice, however, and more closely considered its performance does not come up to expectation. There are several reasons for this, which I shall not enumerate here, as I shall perhaps discuss these instruments adequately elsewhere and also explain how they may be improved, as far as possible. In the meantime I shall explain some others which I invented and have used up till now, instruments that are convenient to use and that give the necessary accuracy. First, as an example of an instrument which can measure smaller distances up to one-twelfth of the circumference of the circle, or, as it is called, one sign of the zodiac, we show in the accompanying figure [Fig. 15] one such instrument.

In the first place we see a flat alidade, beginning at F and ending at the cross-bar BA. Its length is four cubits [155 cm, cf. p. 9], and it carries on the cross-bar mentioned two cylinders at A and B, which are at equal distances from the point where the cross-bar is connected with the alidade. Two arcs FC and FD are drawn below from the point F, with their centres at the centres of the cylinders A and B. Each of these arcs is provided with a division outside a section, the length of which is equal to one-half of AB, and which extends equal lengths from F in both directions.

10

This section ought to have the designation KI (though the figure does not show this correctly). The divisions are reckoned, beginning at IC, or KD, and they extend to both sides covering fifteen degrees. The rest, which is denoted by CG and DH, as well as that which is in between at L, etc., is a grating added for support, as well as for decoration. This instrument rests upon a thick, round support, denoted by TRSQ, which is provided with a quadrangular hole in the middle at E, where the centre of gravity is located. It is fastened to this support by means of a tenon, which is also quadrangular. The support is constructed in the following way. At S and T, and also at Q and R, are round iron plates turning on a round cylinder which supports them, and the diameter of which is somewhat more than a span [cf. p. 9]. Small springs are placed at four points mentioned, keeping the cylinder fixed, whatever position it may have. In this way it is possible only to turn the whole instrument up and down. If it has to be turned sideways, or back again, this can be done by revolving the semicircle ONM, and fastening it with a small screw at N. In this way the whole instrument is also turned. It is also possible to turn it to and fro towards any azimuth by means of the tube PV, which surrounds its round axis. This tube is supported by another base, denoted by V and the letters X, and upon this base the tube together with the whole instrument can be turned in any direction as required in order to make the plane of the instrument coincide with that of any two stars to be observed. The axis that is inside this tube and the tube itself, together with the instrument resting on it, can be raised relatively to the supporting base, and then be fastened in the required position. For within the rectangular base is a strong wooden piece, also rectangular, which can be raised or lowered, and fastened in any desired position. In this way the whole instrument may be raised or lowered according to the altitude of the stars whose angular distance is to be measured. The divided limbs as well as the cross-bar and the cylinders of the instrument are of brass, but the framework and the supports are in finely worked iron. The rest is skilfully made of wood and is covered with metal plates in those places where this is required in order that the whole instrument be rigid and suitable for making observations.

The use of the instrument is, as has been said, for measuring smaller distances, since this cannot very easily be done with the aid of a sextant (about which later). For two observers are needed and the two heads that have to work side by side must have sufficient room. This drawback has been removed, it is true, by another expedient, to be mentioned later. In order to measure with this instrument stellar distances which are not more than one-twelfth of the circumference of the circle, one observer has to set the pinnule at K or I, as is most convenient, while the other observer moves the pinnule which is not fixed, along the outer rim, until both observers sight the two stars they are observing on both sides along the cylinders B and A, respectively, each of them using the cylinder on his own side. Then they have to read the required distance on the lower rim, in degrees and minutes according to the method of transversal points, and from the proper pinnule. If, however, the two observers move both pinnules, then it is possible in the same way to find a yet greater distance, still not exceeding the given limit. It follows from this that, when the two observers each set their pinnules to the zero point of his division, at K or I, respectively, and thus from both sides sight along the front cylinders A and B, in such a way that each of them sights along his own cylinder, namely, that which is on the same side of the long alidade, then they will sight the same star, since their lines of sight are parallel. In this way the reliability of the instrument may be tested and it may be seen whether it is in good working order or not. Although the base of this instrument is sufficiently well constructed and suits the requirements, there is yet another method, in which a spherical body is used (about which we shall speak later in decribing the sextant), and this is more practical and enables the observer to set the instrument more quickly in the plane of any two stars. About this it may be said that variety is not only the spice of life, but also useful.

This instrument I have used primarily for determining the mutual distances of the stars in Cassiopeia, as has been developed in the fourth chapter of our *Astronomiae instaurandae Progymnasmata*, p. 145 and the following page [should be 345, Opera Omnia II, p. 337 f.], and comparing them with those previously found, as long as the new star, which gave the occasion for measuring these distances, was still visible. I found that they had been correctly determined. Anybody who has an instrument with which he thinks that he can measure angular distances between the stars is advised to try the same stars in Cassiopeia and see whether he finds the distances between them equal to those given by us in the place mentioned, and that within one, or even one-half, of a minute of arc. If this is not the case it means that the instrument which he is using, and the method according to which his observations are made, are incorrect.

SEXTANS ASTRONOMICUS TRIGO-
NICUS PRO DISTANTIIS RIMANDIS

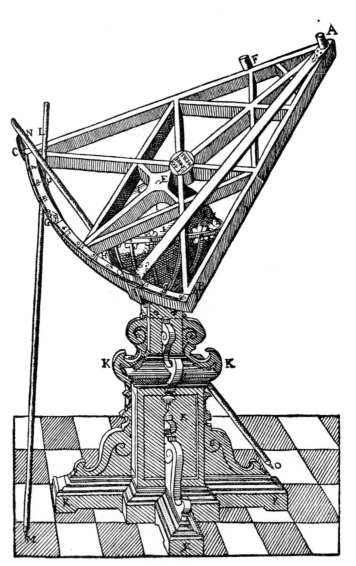

Fig. 16.

SEXTANS ASTRONOMICUS TRIGONICUS PRO DISTANTIIS RIMANDIS

THE TRIANGULAR ASTRONOMICAL SEXTANT FOR THE DETERMINATION OF DISTANCES

DESCRIPTION AND USE OF THE INSTRUMENT

I now come to the explanation of the Astronomical Sextant, since this is particularly suited for the determination of distances in the sky between the stars. For, having found through the experience of many years that the Astronomical Radius by no means sufficed for the solution of the problem with reasonable certainty and accuracy, I devised, driven by necessity, some sextants of different form which solved this problem accurately and without uncertainty. Among these sextants those which are of the construction here presented to the reader, have appeared to me to be the most suitable, and I therefore had three of this kind made, with small differences in the framework only. It is explained as follows. The system within ABC shows the sextant proper with its wooden frame. At the centre near A a cylinder is placed. The periphery CB comprises one-sixth of a circle. The sides AB and AC hold it at a distance of four cubits [155 cm, cf. p. 9] from the centre. Through the very centre of the circular arc passes the alidade AD which has its pinnule near D, with slits parallel to the fixed cylinder at A. This alidade is movable along the periphery, and it can be clamped, as may be desired. The instrument is provided with yet another cylinder, fixed near F and of the same size as that just mentioned. This cylinder is used in connection with another pinnule shown at G. The latter can be attached or removed as desired. The framework has been built with a view to solidity in the way shown in the figure [Fig. 16]. Near E is a quadrangular hole, that is placed at the equilibrium point of the whole instrument, so to speak, in order that it should be possible with the aid of this to fix the sextant to the support, and to remove it again after the observations have been completed. The graduated arc of the sextant is provided with transversal divisions. It is possible to estimate one-quarter of a minute of arc. The arc is made entirely of brass, as are also the cylinders and the pinnules. The other parts are only wooden, but they have been combined and joined together in such an ingenious way—as we have described above, when we explained the armillae—that they cannot bend or change with changes of the air, and furthermore the whole is covered with painted canvas. For if all the various parts of the sextant were covered with sheet-metal, the instrument would become difficult to handle on account of its excessive weight. Also, due to the weight of the instrument it would be difficult to keep it in the correct plane. The base or foundation upon which the sextant rests consists of an exactly spherical globe I, sheeted with copper, the diameter of which is a little over two feet [52 cm, cf. p. 9]. This globe is surrounded by four semicircular iron bands which are attached, at eight points, to an iron ring, the plane of which passes through the centre of the globe. All these points are a little over one inch [cf. p. 9] from the globe inside, for at each of the eight points where the iron bands surround the ring there is an iron screw pressing a star-shaped round piece of sheet-metal against the globe so that it acts like a spring. This is in order that the globe be securely held by the screws and stay in the same place, however it may be turned around.

The semicircular iron bands carry yet another such spring in the middle underneath—the ninth—upon which the globe rests in quite a practical way. This spring is fixed on to a quadratic wooden pillar with the aid of a hollow quadrangular piece of iron. The pillar passes through the base, which is seen near the letter K, in such a way that it can be raised or lowered within it, and clamped in a desired position, with a view to the convenience of the observations. When measuring distances low in the sky one lowers the pillar, for higher ones it is raised, in order that the sighting be made without difficulty. Further, as was mentioned above, the sextant proper is fastened to the globe below it at the hole denoted by E and can be turned around with the greatest ease into any plane passing through two stars. Two long round staffs IM and NO, provided with iron spikes at M and O to secure a good support on the floor, are used to keep the instrument securely in position until the observation has been completed. They cross above at P. One of the observers holds them fast with his hand and guides them as desired.

The use of the instrument requires two observers. One of these puts his eye to the pinnule C and from there through its slits sights a star along the cylinder A. He then keeps the sextant fixed with the aid of the staffs at P. It is assumed that the plane of the sextant passes through that of the two stars, the distances of which are to be measured. This is ensured with the help of the globe on which the sextant is turned until both stars are seen in its plane. The second observer then moves the alidade with its pinnule at D until he, too, can sight the other star on both sides of the cylinder A. This has to be tried to and fro until both observers at one and the same time each sights his star. Having called to each other they stop the observation, and the graduated arc of the sextant is turned on the spherical support towards the eye of one of the observers, so that he can conveniently read the distance between the two pinnules, which was what he sought. Further we have invented a short cut in order to make it possible to measure with the same sextant smaller distances also. A second cylinder is placed at F, and a second pinnule at G. These two are at the same distance from the line AE connecting the centre and the central point of the arc. The first observer sights this cylinder with the pinnule mentioned, while the second observer uses the pinnule D and the cylinder A. The distance between the two stars is then to be read from the central point of the limb at 30 degrees to the pinnule D. In this way nothing will prevent two observers from measuring a distance, however small it may be. If the reader wants further information concerning this instrument he is referred to the first part of my astronomical *Progymnasmata*, p. 247 and the three subsequent pages [Opera Omnia, Vol. II, p. 247—250]. There he will find a more detailed development on this subject, namely that the instrument can be used in many ways for the determination of stellar angular distances, a subject that I have described precisely in the second chapter of the work mentioned, and treated according to the astronomical methods. For I can certify that this instrument gives the stellar distances with such certainty and accuracy, and so quickly and easily, that it leaves nothing to be desired. This will be clear if for instance the stellar distances given and applied on p. 195—203 [Opera Omnia II, p. 198—206] in the book mentioned are carefully studied. Here it is seen, when the differences of right ascension, obtained by means of the declinations of the stars with the aid of triangles, are added, that the instrument exactly comprises and closes the whole circle. This would not have been possible if concealed errors were present. Therefore this method of observation of stellar distances with the aid of such a sextant is recommended to those who wish to learn this art.

SEXTANS CHALYBEUS PRO DISTAN-
TIIS PER UNICUM OBSERVATOREM DIMETIENDIS

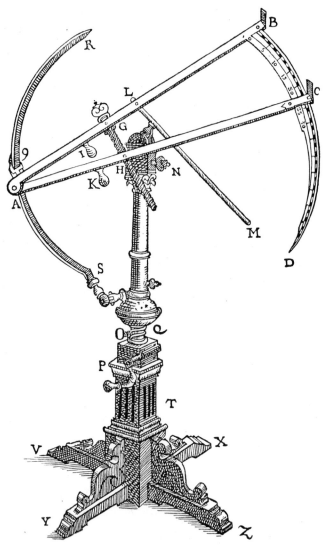

Fig. 17.

SEXTANS CHALYBEUS PRO DISTANTIIS PER UNICUM OBSERVATOREM DIMETIENDIS

STEEL SEXTANT FOR MEASURING DISTANCES BY ONE SINGLE OBSERVER

DESCRIPTION AND USE OF THE INSTRUMENT

I had already previously constructed another sextant, made of massive steel, and designed in such a way that one observer with its help could determine sufficiently easily the angular distances of the stars. Besides, this instrument, not only the sextant proper but also its base, can be taken apart, and put together again by means of convenient screws, so that it can be packed in a case and if necessary transported to other regions, as I did in my youth about 24 years ago, when I travelled through Germany. Its construction can be inferred, approximately, from the figure [Fig. 17]. A more detailed explanation we may borrow from the second book of our Progymnasmata, summarising its main features. Towards the end of that book the same instrument is delineated and described. The sextant proper is denoted by ABCD and its centre is at A, while the corresponding arc BD is divided into 60 degrees and their single minutes by transversals according to our custom. The alidades AB and AC of the instrument are connected with each other at A by a round pivot, so that one can separate them or bring them closer together, as with the legs of a pair of compasses. This is done with the aid of a screw, denoted by the letters GH, which, although it is straight, yet at the points where it is joined to the alidades moves firmly in nuts that can be turned in all directions, so that it is quite suitable in spite of the curved motion of the instrument. The instrument also carries two handles, denoted by the letters IK, which are grasped when sights are made. B and C are two pinnules. When the eye which is close to the centre A is directed towards these, it observes two stars at the same time, the angle BAC being made larger or smaller with the aid of the screw GH. In that case the arc BC will show the required distance, it being necessary, however, to subtract the parallax of the instrument. Besides I found later on a means by which it is possible to make parallel sights as with other diopters and pinnules. Then the subtraction of a parallax is unnecessary.

But since this construction of the diopters is not shown here, I have decided to explain it on another occasion, when this same sextant appears fitted with such diopters. Furthermore, it has a base with the aid of which the sextant can be brought into any plane with still greater ease. The alidades AB and AC of this sextant measure about three cubits [117 cm, cf. p. 9], and the length of the arc BD, which they span, is the same. The entire sextant is ingeniously worked in solid steel, the pinnules only being of brass. It rests upon a support, or base, in order to be more convenient in use, and more manageable when observations are to be made. The construction is as follows. Firstly, the instrument rests solidly on the earth upon its cruciform base VXYZ. Just above it is something like a hollow leg at T, into which a long screw is stuck at Q, and with the aid of another endless screw, lying inside at P, this can be raised or lowered as desired, and with it the sextant proper. Both screws are of solid iron, as is the entire upper part of the support. The round piece of iron HO, which is hollow inside, turns around another oblong axis connected with the screw Q by a knob seen at the same place, so that it can be held, if desired, by a screw at O. This round piece of iron has a quadrangular knob on top of it, out of which protrudes a spike to which is fixed another long piece of iron, denoted by the letters LM. The sextant proper is fixed to the latter at L and can slide along it until it reaches its outermost end. This knob is quadrangular and inside ingeniously provided with small wheels in such a way that when its screw at N is turned, then the spike mentioned by means of the inner wheel communicates to the flat piece of iron LM with the whole of the sextant connected to it an inclination sideways in either direction according to the position of the two stars. It is also possible with the aid of the arc SR, which is connected with, and stuck into, the round tube OH mentioned at S in a special way, to raise or lower the centre at A, together with the whole sextant, as required by the higher or lower position of the star. The instrument can then be fixed to this arc by means of a screw placed on the far side at 9. All this, however, is much easier to understand, when one sees and handles the instrument. With this instrument, which I had constructed many years ago, I have measured angular distances of stars, and I used it particularly for the observations of the comet of the year 1577. This is the reason why this sextant is, as was mentioned, delineated and described in greater detail towards the end of the lucid book that we wrote on this comet. Anybody who might wish to do so may read more about it in the place mentioned pp. 459—461 [Opera Omnia IV, pp. 369 —371].

The use of the instrument is for measuring angular distances of the stars up to one-sixth of the circumference of the circle, and that with one observer who, having placed his eye near the centre at A, and having adjusted the whole sextant according to the plane of the stars with the aid of the screws of the base, then turns the screw GH towards one side or the other, thus increasing or diminishing the angle BAC, until the two stars are distinguished with perfect accuracy through the pinnules BC. The division of the arc BD will then indicate the required distance between them. To begin with the circumference had in addition to the usual division a Nonnian division, but when experience taught me that another method of division, namely the one that makes use of transversal points, is much more convenient and accurate, I gave up the methods previously used and applied the latter. I constructed the circumference of the sextant of brass, in order that it should not, like steel, easily become rusty, and completed the division according to my custom, marking ten points in a slanting line for every sixth of one degree. In this way it became more convenient to use. The importance, however, of angular distances of the stars in astronomical problems is treated both in my own writings and in those of other authors. For their use is very extensive, and the observations of the comet mentioned, which are treated in the second chapter of the book quoted above, and made with precisely this sextant, present examples of such problems, which in the next chapter are solved by solutions of spherical triangles.

Once during the year 1580 when the distinguished mathematician Paul Wittich of Breslau had been shown this sextant while with me, he made it known, later on, to the illustrious prince, the landgrave Wilhelm of Hesse, etc., of glorious memory. The latter then let his able mechanic construct a similar instrument, a few changes being made, however, either of things which Wittich did not quite remember, or else because they were of a different opinion. For instead of the screw G they introduced a chain with the aid of which it was possible to increase or diminish the angle of the instrument. The method of division they preserved without a change, however, as Wittich had been taught it by me. The construction has been imitated since then by others, and some have even attributed the invention to themselves, as has also been the case with many other things of mine. The value of this instrument has been proved in a splendid way by the fact that the distances found by its aid in Cassel agree within a minute, indeed within one-half of a minute, with those found by us in Denmark with our sextants, as can be seen from the first volume of our astronomical letters [Opera Omnia VI, pp. 66 and 91].

ALIUD INSTRUMENTUM SIMILE
PRIORI, PRO DISTANTIIS

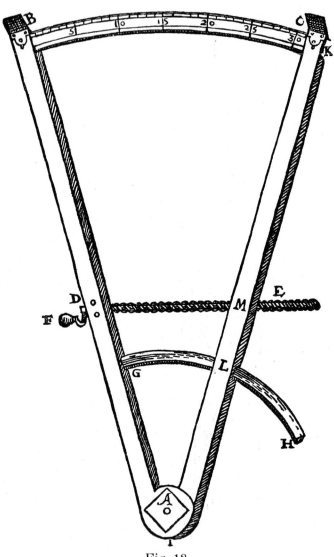

Fig. 18.

ALIUD INSTRUMENTUM SIMILE PRIORI, PRO DISTANTIIS

ANOTHER INSTRUMENT OF THE SAME KIND AS THE PREVIOUS ONE, FOR MEASURING ANGULAR DISTANCES

DESCRIPTION AND USE OF THE INSTRUMENT

At an earlier period in my youth when I spent some time in Augsburg in upper Germany, I had already procured for myself such an instrument, which however was made of wood only and had no base, it being so light that it could be turned around as desired without any such support. On going away I left it as a present for the mayor of this mighty town, Paul Hainzel, who highly deserves remembrance on account of his great interest in these studies, and who was a close friend of mine. Afterwards, when shortly after my return to my fatherland this new and extremely admirable star had begun shining in the sky, I had a similar instrument made for myself in order to be able to measure accurately its angular distances from the neighbouring stars in Cassiopeia. You see here a delineation of this instrument [Fig. 18]. The divided arc is denoted by BC. It comprises one-twelfth of the circumference of a circle only, or 30 degrees, because that would be sufficient for smaller distances such as those we have just mentioned, and because it would not then be heavy and difficult to manage on account of its length. It is possible however to substitute other arcs for this one, either longer or shorter as desired. The alidades AB and AC which are connected at the centre A, where they can turn about each other, and which span the circumference BC, are four cubits long [155 cm, cf. p. 9], three inches wide [cf. p. 9] and two inches thick. They are of quadrangular cross section and are made of very dry walnut wood, which is less influenced by climatic conditions than any other kind of wood. At the place where the alidades are connected with each other around the centre A, they are kept together by means of a tenon and a hole; they are completely worked into one another, and are also strengthened by some small bronze sheets. The arc itself is solidly built of metal, neither too thick nor too wide, however, in order to avoid any harmful effects due to excessive weight. In this way one avoids disturbances due to changes in the wood. The pinnules at BC are also of brass and constructed in such a way that their inner sides correspond exactly with the inner surfaces of the alidades, and on the other, lower side is a screw with the aid of which the movable pinnule may be clamped when the observation has been made until the reading on the arc has been completed. There is also another long screw at DE, by means of which the angle BAC of the instrument may be diminished or increased, as required by the distance to be measured. Although this screw is straight, it is yet suitable for the curved motion taking place at DE with A as centre, since it is provided with nuts on the other side which can turn about some small round pivots, as we have explained in connection with the previous instrument. Inside this screw, nearer the centre and the eye, an arc GLH is mounted on the first alidade at G, passing through the other at L. Its function is to keep the two alidades in their plane, in order that they should not on account of their lengths be pulled sideways. The reverse side of the same arc is constructed so that it can keep the angle of the instrument constant. The distance from the centre is about one-third of the length of the alidades, so that by placing one hand there, one can conveniently hold the alidades, or control their motions. On the reverse side the arc has, further, two handles which are not shown in the figure. At the time I did not construct any base for the instrument. Since however it was not very heavy, it was possible, when supporting it on a cross-piece, to bring it into the plane of any two stars without particular difficulty, and to keep it there until the observation had been made.

The use of the instrument is the same as that of the previous one. The eye is placed near I, and the handle F is turned. On turning the screw DE, one increases or diminishes the angle BAC until the two stars, the distance of which is required, are seen accurately and centrally within the pinnules B and C. For then the arc between the two pinnules and the alidades indicates to the observer what he seeks to find. Since, however, the centre of vision does not coincide with the centre of the instrument, which latter determines the divisions, the fixed piece from A to I preventing this, the distances measured and read on the arc, the eye being placed outside the centre, must necessarily be too great, and greater than those that are in agreement with the sky itself.

In order to remedy this drawback I had constructed a table and recorded it on the reverse side of the instrument in order that it should always be at hand. It showed the parallax of the instrument, namely the amount to be subtracted from every degree indicated by the observations to produce the true distance agreeing with the sky, and precisely that which would have been found from the centre of the instrument, had the centre of vision coincided with it. The way in which this table was calculated, using the theorems of plane triangles, is explained by us in the first volume of our *Progymnasmata instaurationis astronomicae*, in the fourth chapter p. 342 [Opera Omnia II, pp. 330—336]. A thorough description of this instrument is also found there, pp. 335—343, and any reader who might wish to know more about it is referred to this. There, a little further on, he will also find the distances between the new star and the neighbouring stars in Cassiopeia and various others, and also some mutual distances of stars, measured with great accuracy with this instrument and employed in practice. For at the time I had ready no other instrument suitable for this purpose, as I had only recently returned from my journey in Germany, and was more occupied in chemical than in astronomical studies.

Although this instrument is not as excellent as those that I invented and had constructed in later years with much trouble and at great cost, and though I subsequently rejected it, yet I think that such as it is, and since it is not inconvenient to use, it ought to be delineated and described here together with the other instruments. Hereby I hope to serve those who are not in a position to have such intricate and costly instruments constructed. They must therefore be content with this one, which gives greater correctness and accuracy than the astronomical radius of former times, when angular distances of the stars are to be determined. The important thing is that they take account of the parallax, I have spoken about, speedily and in the correct way.

INSTRUMENTI EIUSDEM UT AL-
TITUDINIBUS CAPIENDIS INSERVIAT DISPOSITIO

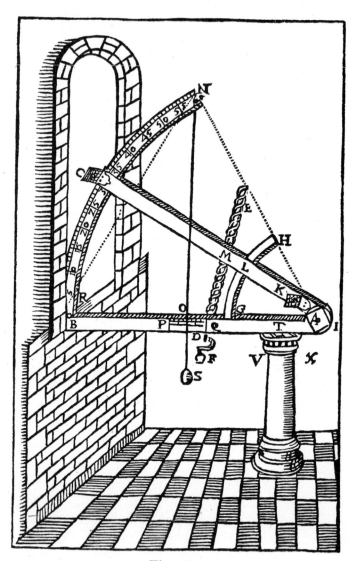

Fig. 19.

INSTRUMENTI EIUSDEM UT ALTITUDINIBUS CAPIENDIS INSERVIAT DISPOSITIO

MOUNTING OF THE SAME INSTRUMENT FOR OBSERVATIONS OF ALTITUDES

DESCRIPTION AND USE OF THE INSTRUMENT

The same instrument is not unsuitable for observations of altitudes of stars, particularly if its arc comprises one-sixth of the circumference of the circle, provided it is mounted as shown in the accompanying figure [Fig. 19]. In this fashion I measured the minimum altitude of the new star which was seen in the year 1572 and the following year, as it passed the meridian below the pole. For it was not possible to measure its maximum altitude near the zenith with this instrument, since this wonderful star at our geographical latitude was not far from the zenith when on the meridian above the pole, so that its altitude exceeded one-sixth of the circumference of the circle. This and similar circumstances are apparent from the book previously quoted, in the same chapter as given there [Opera Omnia II, p. 339 —342]. The way in which I made the observations (also explained in the same place) was as follows. This sextant was with its lower alidade AB mounted in a high window on top of a wall R, so that it pointed exactly towards the celestial meridian in which the observation was to be made. Below the instrument a support denoted by the letters VX stood beneath the back of the alidade near the centre at T, and its height was so adjusted that the alidade proper AB was exactly horizontal. This I ascertained in the following way. I set the arc RN of the instrument with its alidades in the plane of the meridian, and at the end of it, where the 60 degrees of the division also end, I suspended a plumb-line at N denoted by NS. I then raised or lowered the lower alidade AB, as far as this was necessary, by means of some wedges between T and VX, and with the alidade the whole instrument also, until the brass wire NOS, to which is fastened a piece of lead at S, exactly touched a point O half-way between the centre of the sextant A and the arc. From this it is clear that the alidade of the instrument, or the base line AB, will be exactly horizontal, since according to elementary Geometry (as is proved in Euclid's fourth book, the fifteenth theorem) one-sixth of the circle with the centre as the vertex gives an isosceles [equilateral] triangle, formed by the dotted lines RNA and the alidade AB as the third side. Since the straight line, descending from N and pointing towards the zenith, divides the base line, RA, into two equal parts, it follows that it must necessarily cut it at right angles, as is apparent from the twelfth theorem in the first book and those immediately preceding it. Since, consequently, the plumb-line, NS, points always towards the zenith, and the line NO coincides with it, the alidade RA must make a whole right angle with this plumb-line, and it must therefore also be parallel to the horizon, which on all sides has a distance from the zenith amounting to a quarter of the circumference of a circle, which corresponds to a right angle. When in this way everything was adjusted and arranged with the greatest possible care, I watched for the moment when the new star, as a consequence of the rotation of the celestial sphere reached the meridian at its lower culmination, and then I sighted it through another pinnule corresponding to the forward pinnule at C, which was mounted on the alidade at K not very far from the centre, and which could be removed if that was necessary. For at the upper end of this other pinnule was a slit passing through the centre and parallel with the upper rim of the forward pinnule. Looking through this I altered the angle of the instrument by turning the long screw DE, until I could distinguish the new star exactly on the upper rim of the pinnule at C, or rather until I could see half of it, the other half being hidden, as far as such sharp visibility was possible. (I had not yet invented the system of parallel slits in both pinnules which enables the centre of a star to be sighted with the greatest accuracy.) In this way I found, from the arc between the pinnules B and C, the minimum altitude of the star above the horizon, as I have shown in the place quoted from the book mentioned above [Opera Omnia II, p. 341]. It could easily happen, however that the alidade BA, and with it the whole sextant, lost its proper horizontal adjustment during the observations, if the supports upon which the instrument rested shifted a little to one side or the other on account of the wedges inserted in it. A few divisions of a small arc, PQ, described with N as the centre, were therefore placed along a line through that point, O, in the middle of the lower alidade which the plumb-line of the instrument was to touch if the adjustment was correct, in such a way that one degree had the proper length corresponding to the diameter of the circle, the degree being divided on both sides of O into minutes of arc. If now the plumb-line touched a point on the part OP of this division in front of O, the number of minutes indicating the deviation from O of the plumb-line was to be subtracted from the altitude, while if the plumb-line touched a point on the part OQ behind O the correction was to be added. In this way I checked the altitude indicated on the arc BC, reading the position of the plumb-line after the observation had been completed, and correcting the altitude when this appeared to me to be necessary in order to determine it with greater accuracy. Although it would have been possible to carry out the observations more accurately, by sighting through two parallel slits close to the eye and the forward pinnule, yet it is possible by the method just described to obtain results of sufficient accuracy, particularly if the sighting of one and the same star is repeated several times, as I did with the new star, which remained at the same altitude in the meridian without any appreciable change for the whole period of its visibility. What has here been stated in connexion with this star as an example must be understood to hold good in the same way for altitudes of other stars, provided only that the altitude does not exceed one-sixth of the circumference of the circle, and not only for stars in the meridian but in any vertical circle. The plane of the instrument must, of course, coincide with the plane of this circle, and for the rest everything must be carried out as indicated above.

The use of the instrument for observations of altitudes also will be clear from what has been said. As a matter of fact however it is possible to obtain with quadrants, particularly with the larger ones that I have already mentioned, results of greater accuracy, and with less trouble. Anyone not having at his disposal such instruments which are very expensive may however make use of the instrument that we have just described, or a similar one to which we drew attention before when dealing with measurements of angular distances by means of these instruments. But an experienced observer must be cautious with these instruments, and the sighting of them, for they get out of adjustment easily, and errors somehow slip in from one cause or another. For very small quantities are in question from which conclusions of the greatest importance are drawn, and care must be taken not to waste the time and effort expended which most modern astronomers in fact do. I only wish that, in cases requiring extreme accuracy the same doubts did not arise with regard to the ancients; for then it would indeed be possible to develop in a more satisfactory way an Astronomy valid for all time. How great a contribution towards this end is found in the observations and opinions of our predecessors it has been, and will still be, my aim to show with the help of the most High, that the whole may emerge free from error and in complete perfection.

88

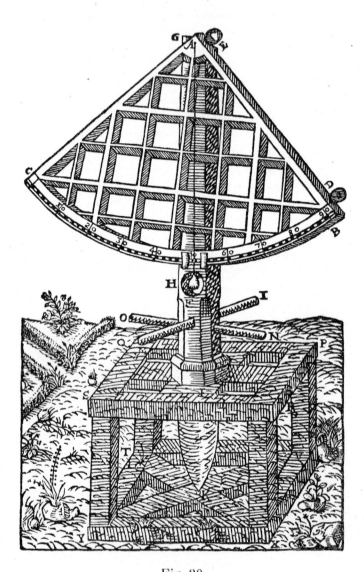

QUADRANS MAXIMUS QUALEM OLIM
PROPE AUGUSTAM VINDELICORUM EXSTRUXIMUS

Fig. 20.

QUADRANS MAXIMUS QUALEM OLIM PROPE AUGUSTAM VINDELICORUM EXSTRUXIMUS

THE GREAT QUADRANT WHICH WE CONSTRUCTED AT ONE TIME IN THE NEIGHBOURHOOD OF AUGSBURG

DESCRIPTION AND USE OF THE INSTRUMENT

I think that I will also add a delineation and description of the great quadrant which we had constructed 26 years ago in Master Paul Hainzel's garden on his property half a mile from Augsburg, although it does not exist any more, having been left derelict five years after it had been constructed. Anybody who might wish to have a similar instrument constructed will, I think, have something to guide him, so that it is worth while to add this direction. This quadrant together with the framework that is built into it, is denoted by ACB. It was made entirely of oak that had been dried through many years. The sides as well as the framework were made of heavy beams. The radius of the instrument, i. e. the distance from the centre to the circumference, measured at least 14 cubits [543 cm, cf. p. 9]. On the rim, i. e. on the circumference where the divisions were located, it was covered with brass sheets. The built in framework consisted of cross-beams joined together and smoothed, and constructed for the purpose of keeping the whole quadrant the more rigidly together and hold it in its proper shape and plane. The division of the arc was made in the customary way. For at that time I had not yet invented the other more convenient method which I used later on for other instruments. Still it was possible not only to divide every degree into single minutes of arc, but even to subdivide every minute into six small parts, so that the divisions made it possible to distinguish a quantity so small as ten seconds of arc. On one side, DE, of the quadrant, where the observer stood, pinnules were mounted at D. Of these the one closest to the eye had a small hole in the middle, through which the stars could be distinguished in the upper pinnule at E along its diameter. When the sun was to be observed, another pierced pinnule was used in the forward position at E, which through a round hole admitted the rays of the sun within a circular mark placed on the inner side of the lower pinnule the diameter of which matched the image, and to this was further added an oblong tube to prevent the scattering in the air of the light of the sun, and to make it the more clearly visible within the limits of this circular mark. In addition a thin brass wire was fastened at the centre A of the instrument which was able to carry a weight of a few pounds seen in front of a hole H so that the wire should not so easily be disturbed by the wind. For it was precisely this wire which, touching the arc, indicated with the greatest accuracy the required altitude.

This quadrant was supported at its centre, A, by a thick and strong oak column joined to it by a strong, round piece of iron that was fastened on the far side at G. The rim was further supported by two small hooks, mounted slightly above the hole where the lead of the plumb-line was located. The purpose of these was to keep the whole quadrant in position pressed against the column, after it had been raised or lowered to the position required by the observation, so that it would not swing back under its own weight, before the reading of the observed altitude had been completed. The lower end of the column was rigidly connected with an underground construction XYSPK, within which it could turn around. For it was provided with a steel point underneath, which at K could turn easily within a hole of corresponding form, located below the point. Further up the column was on all sides supported in a conical hole, so that it could not shift, and yet could revolve perfectly together with the quadrant which it carried. The turning of the instrument into any vertical plane in question was carried out with the aid of the handles QOIN, and the quadrant, as a consequence of its great weight remained immovable in any desired vertical plane. Everything seen below the handles was covered with earth, firmly beaten down and supported by stones underneath as well as all around in order the more securely to carry the whole instrument above and keep it in position so that it did not move towards one side or the other. For the instrument was entirely in the open and thus exposed to the wind and the damaging influence of the air. It was however covered, especially the arc, in order that the divisions should not suffer.

The use of the instrument was exclusively for observations of the altitudes of the sun and the planets, and that with the greatest accuracy, in fact within one-sixth of a minute of arc, provided the observer exercised the necessary care. A similar accuracy had hardly ever been reached by our predecessors. It is true that we obtained the same accuracy later on with instruments that were smaller, but distinguished by other merits in the construction. When an altitude was to be measured, the observer held his eye close to the pinnule at D, and then looked for the star in the other, or forward pinnule by raising or lowering the quadrant until he saw it there. If the altitudes were too low, he was obliged to use a ladder to stand on. If he then let the instrument remain in its position he could read the required altitude at the wire of the plumb-line on the circular arc. This must now suffice as far as the construction and use of the instrument is concerned.

Anybody who might wish for more detailed instructions will find this in the first volume of our *Progymnasmata*, pp. 353—359 [Opera Omnia II, pp. 342—347]. In the same place the altitudes of the new star are given on the following pages, together with the altitudes of certain other stars recorded with the aid of this instrument by the above-mentioned mayor, Paul Hainzel, for my purposes, and later on communicated to me by him. From this a competent person may ascertain the accuracy of the observations, and these altitudes also agreed perfectly with those that I measured later on in Denmark with other instruments. One could have wished that this excellent instrument had been preserved for a longer period in this place, and had stayed in use, or, else, that another instrument had been constructed in its place. Since however men as a rule are more interested in worldly matters than in things celestial, they usually regard with indifference such happenings which will perhaps be more harmful to them than they themselves realize.

QUADRANS MAXIMUS CHALYBEUS
QUADRATO INCLUSUS, ET HORIZONTI AZIMUTHALI
CHALYBEO INSISTENS

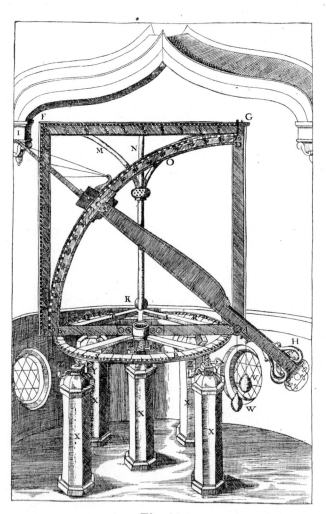

Fig. 21.

QUADRANS MAXIMUS CHALYBEUS QUADRATO INCLUSUS, ET HORIZONTI AZIMUTHALI CHALYBEO INSISTENS

GREAT STEEL QUADRANT, CONFINED IN A SQUARE, AND STANDING ON AN AZIMUTH HORIZON OF STEEL

DESCRIPTION AND USE OF THE INSTRUMENT

This quadrant we have in fact described among the instruments delineated under No. 7 [p. 37, cf. also p. 43], but it was there mounted in a different way so that it revolved within a brick crypt around a strong steel axis pointing towards the zenith and the nadir, and it had further, within the circumference of the subterranean wall, a strong azimuth ring which has been sufficiently delineated and described together with the remaining accessories in the place mentioned. Since however I there promised that I would on a later occasion explain another way of mounting it, which I had made use of in the beginning, it is given here. It may be briefly described in the following way. ABCD is the quadrant proper [Fig. 21], described about A as centre, and confined in the square AEFG. Its alidade ACI is prolonged at the lower end to the handle H, where a pinnule is found provided with slits parallel to the upper pinnule at C. At the upper end it is prolonged from C to I, so that it everywhere reaches the square. At the upper end some brass wires are fastened at I serving the purpose of supporting the pointer so that it will everywhere stay straight. What can be seen behind this, or ALMNO, is an iron support that holds the entire quadrant in a position at right angles to the horizontal plane below it. For at A it is connected with an azimuth horizon, and below the latter is a small screw provided with a spring, like a clip, in order that it may be turned around as desired on the azimuth circle with the aid of a handle on the far side. The azimuth circle mentioned is denoted by the letters PQRS. Five strong columns denoted by X carry the whole instrument. At the capitals YZ are endless screws with revolving handles, by means of which the azimuth circle is kept horizontal, and the whole quadrant adjusted in a vertical plane as indicated by the plumb-lines denoted by V and W. The rest is apparent from what has been explained above in the place mentioned, where this very quadrant was mounted in another and rather more convenient way. Therefore, I do not care to repeat more about this for the sake of explanation, in order not to bore the reader by serving up the same things that have been said before.

But in order that the space below this may be filled in, as before, a poem in hexameters has now been added which the distinguished and learned young man, Franciscus Gansneb Tengnagel who once served with me and accompanied me on my journey from Denmark has extemporized so that it might be added here. [The poem is omitted in this translation].

DE ALIIS QUIBUSDAM INSTRUMENTIS NOSTRIS QUÆ NONDUM EXSCULPTA SUNT, BREVIS INDICATIO

OF SOME OTHER OF OUR INSTRUMENTS, WHICH HAVE NOT YET BEEN DELINEATED, A BRIEF REGISTER IS HERE GIVEN

Up to now we have exhibited and described our astronomical instruments in so far as drawings and woodcuts of them already made rendered this possible at the time. I have at my disposal yet a few others which I have been obliged to omit here as they have not yet been drawn and cut. I shall however take pains to have them added to the rest as soon as possible, and in order that this treatise on the mechanical part of Astronomy be made more copious I also wish to add some accessories and tables serving the same purpose. Meanwhile I shall here briefly present a preliminary account of some of the other instruments.

SEXTANS BIFURCATUS

THE BIFURCATED SEXTANT

We have also constructed a sextant which has been given the name of the bifurcated sextant because it is provided with alidades on both sides of the centre, the angle between which can be diminished or increased, as they cut each other crosswise. This instrument has an arc of steel that spans one-sixth of the circumference of the sky. The alidades are four cubits long [155 cm, cf. p. 9]. Brass pinnules are mounted in various ways on both sides outside the centre near the ends of the alidades. The alidades are of Brazilian wood, since this is firm and durable. On its arc are divisions according to our usual method. With this sextant it is possible to measure angular distances of stars with sufficient accuracy, each of two observers using the pinnule on his proper alidade. It is, however, rather more difficult to make the observations with this sextant than with the others, and they take more time. Nevertheless, as it is easy to transport it has its uses.

SEMICIRCULUS AMPLUS PRO MAIORIBUS DISTANTIIS COELITUS DENOTANDIS
GREAT SEMICIRCLE FOR THE DETERMINATION OF MAJOR ANGULAR DISTANCES IN THE SKY

It is not possible with the sextants invented and constructed by us to measure stellar distances greater than those falling within one-sixth of the circumference of the sky. It sometimes happens that one is obliged to investigate in the sky distances exceeding this limit, and in fact even exceeding a quarter. This is sometimes necessary for observational convenience and usefulness, particularly so in the case of the greater distances between the sun and the moon when they are simultaneously seen in the daytime at both quadratures or at still greater distances, and also on other occasions. I therefore had a semicircular instrument constructed, strengthened all over with cross-beams, and solidly covered with brass plates, on the circumference as well as on the alidade forming the diameter. My purpose was to make it possible by means of this instrument to measure accurately stellar distances of any magnitude, even up to a half of the circumference. The diameter of this semicircle is six cubits [233 cm, cf. p. 9], and in the middle of the instrument, where it is approximately in equilibrium, is a quadrangular hole, in which the semicircle can be fixed to a strong support, preferably spherical, when observations are to be made by two observers who turn it into the plane of the stars. For that matter it is used in the same way as the sextants. Therefore it will not be necessary to add more about it. Anyone who might desire further information may look for it in the explanation of the sextant for measuring distances.

RADIUS ASTRONOMICUS
THE ASTRONOMICAL RADIUS

We do not altogether reject the use of a radius, especially on journeys, since it is easily transported and may be packed into quite a small box, although it is true that it cannot yield quite accurate and certain stellar distances. I have such an instrument at my disposal constructed, not by myself, but by Walter Arscenius, a grandson of the eminent mathematician Gemma Frisius, who at one time lived in Louvain in Belgium, and who has written a small book on it. It is all made of carefully joined brass plates, but inside it is wooden. It has pinnules and divisions as described by Gemma in the book mentioned. The longest alidade, or the radius proper, is a little more than three cubits [117 cm, cf. p. 9] long. It is of quadrangular cross-section, the thickness being in both directions about equal to that of a rather big thumb. The dimensions of the cross-bar are about half of those of the radius proper, both in length and thickness. In addition I had my craftsmen construct another radius also entirely of brass, but hollow, without any wood inside. For wood has the property that if it is not subjected to a special treatment it will force the brass plates with which it is covered to bend in the direction in which the wood itself is bending on account of its own instability and the changing influence of the air. The radius however which we made later, instead of four sides, had but three, because this would reduce its weight, and these three surfaces would suffice for carrying all the divisions. I made equidistant divisions on it, making use of transversal points according to my custom, in order that it might fulfil the same purpose as a five-figure sine-table, and in every respect give better results than Gemma's radius mentioned above, the latter being provided with a non-uniform division arranged in another way which is, incidentally, erroneous. With regard to length and width and other matters it resembles the previous one, and it has the same kind of pinnules. Frankly however, no matter how this radius is constructed it cannot, as I intimated before, give stellar distances precisely in accordance with reality, not even the smaller distances up to 15 degrees, not to mention the greater ones where the error is still larger. It will not be difficult to explain the reason for this on another occasion, but here we shall aim at brevity. Nevertheless I have invented a means, by which it is possible to remove completely the difficulties and errors of the radius, namely by the use of pinnules provided with slits and a cylinder on this instrument also. As with the sextant, distances are then measured by two observers sighting round the cylinder. About this we shall, God willing, say more on another occasion when the instrument is completed, for it is now under construction.

ANNULUS ASTRONOMICUS
THE ASTRONOMICAL RING

We also have an astronomical ring, an instrument which, on account of its being easy to handle, has been used on other occasions by many people, both in ancient and in recent times. It was constructed a few years ago by that same grandson of Gemma's according to the description which the same Gemma gave in his small book. This ring is made entirely of brass and worked with great art. Its diameter is about one cubit [39 cm, cf. p. 9]. To this we have added another invention inside the ring, namely some oblong and round cylinders cutting each other cross-wise at right angles and touching the surface of the inner armilla, where they are fastened to a quadrangular support. Further we have provided the instrument with pinnules and certain other accessories, so that it can yield not only that which Gemma and others have communicated with regard to the use of this ring, and much more, easily at that, but also other things. For in this way it is possible to determine not only, and more conveniently than before, declinations of stars, but also differences of right ascension and right ascensions themselves, not to speak of the longitudes and latitudes of the stars which it is also possible to find by making use of a special method. There is still more, about which I shall, God willing, speak in greater detail when the instrument has been constructed and delineated.

In truth however it is not possible with the aid of such small toy instruments to study the celestial phenomena with sufficient accuracy, because they cannot, on account of their small size, show degrees large enough to permit an exact subdivision into minutes. If on the other hand they are made sufficiently large to make this possible, they become difficult to handle on account of their size and weight. Besides, they are oppressed by their own weight to such an extent that they cannot be used without errors being introduced. We also made another smaller ring of brass, the diameter of which is a little less than a span [cf. p. 9]. However, in my opinion the value of the latter is still less.

The use of such rings is primarily for distinguishing the hours of the night and the day, although they cannot do this as easily and accurately as one would think judging from their appearance. In a way however they are quite suitable for this purpose when other and more dependable instruments are not available, particularly because they are so easy to handle and therefore can be conveniently transported. Anybody who might desire information concerning the other less essential and not very reliable applications that Gemma and others have enumerated, we refer to the books of these authors.

ARMILLA PORTATILIS

THE PORTABLE ARMILLA

We have also constructed an armillary instrument consisting of a single armilla [ring], strengthened however by suitable braces inside it. It is made in such a way that it can easily be transported from one place to another and be erected in the open, together with its stone base and the screws mounted on the latter, so that it is possible with little trouble to turn it towards any direction of the sky. Only declinations of stars can be determined with this instrument, and then not with the same degree of accuracy as with the larger armillary instruments previously discussed. Since however the diameter of this armilla is about three cubits [117 cm, cf. p. 9], and the arc is completely covered with brass, and indicates within every degree each single minute by means of transversal points, it is rather suitable for determining declinations, and I have used it particularly for stars near the horizon, as certain difficulties arise in that case when the walls of the crypts obstruct the vision. Other circumstances also sometimes (in certain special positions) make this instrument more convenient for this work than the larger ones; and there is the further point that observations with different instruments provide a check on the results. It is also possible if desired to mount on this armilla a semicircular equator corresponding to it, together with a round cylindrical axis, thus adapting it for other purposes, namely the determination of right ascensions, and of the time. We occasionally use it in this way.

ASTROLABIUM
THE ASTROLABE

The astrolabe is an instrument that was used by the ancients, particularly by the astrologers. As far as I know, it was first invented by the Arabians in the course of their ingenious investigations. It arranges the circles of the celestial sphere and their use in one plane where they are compressed. I admit I have not hitherto wanted to make an instrument of this kind of suitable size, because neither is it very convenient for observations of the stars, nor adequate and reliable for such purposes. I have a small one, however, which I once bought with my own money, solidly and ingeniously worked in brass, and with a diameter of a little over a span [cf. p. 9]. The instrument with its cylinders is constructed according to the old method explained in detail by Johannes Stöffler and his successors. Anybody who might wish to inform himself on the subject of its construction and use is referred to this source. A few years ago I had a few round brass plates made for me with great care at Nürnberg. The diameter of these plates was more than two cubits [78 cm, cf. p. 9], and they were of a corresponding thickness. My intention was to use them for the construction of a catholic, that is a universal, astrolabe which was to give with fewer cylinders and two surfaces only all that is contained in the theory of the diurnal rotation of the fixed stars, or otherwise conveniently shown on a spherical body, whereas with the aid of this instrument, it is represented in a plane. Therefore I intend to provide it with a special kind of net, and to introduce some of the more important fixed stars on it, in fact many more than the ancients used to have in theirs. This astrolabe may, owing to its convenient construction and careful workmanship, surpass the one invented by de Roias, and also the still more commendable one constructed later by Gemma Frisius, and it will be even more universal. Up to now the work on the construction of other instruments and in connection with many other troublesome tasks has prevented us from building such an astrolabe. We have without regret refrained from doing so, because one cannot by means of it determine the

13*

courses and the positions of the stars with any sufficient degree of accuracy, its use presupposing that these quantities have already been determined by other methods, and for the further reason that we had not yet had those fixed stars that were to be introduced into the astrolabe investigated completely according to our own renewed observations. As we have now, however, by the grace of God, been able to complete these determinations, it will not be difficult to construct such an astrolabe, when we have sufficient time for it, especially as the necessary brass plates, which I once procured for myself, as mentioned above, are still partly available.

DE ALIIS QUIBUSDAM INSTRUMENTIS ASTRONOMICIS; MIRO COMPENDIO MULTA EXPEDIENTIBUS, QUAE NUPER EXCOGITAVI ET SUO TEMPORE FAVENTE NUMINE ELABORARE CONSTITUI

ON A FEW OTHER ASTRONOMICAL INSTRUMENTS, EXTREMELY USEFUL FOR SOLVING MANY PROBLEMS, WHICH I HAVE RECENTLY THOUGHT OUT, AND WHICH I INTEND, GOD WILLING, TO HAVE CONSTRUCTED

All the instruments enumerated in the preceding pages, those that have been delineated and described in detail as well as those that were mentioned briefly afterwards, we have procured for ourselves, so that they are now available to us. It is true that they are so different, and so numerous, that they are perfectly sufficient for all kinds of observations of the celestial bodies. Yet, when I foresaw in my own mind that it would become necessary for me to leave my beloved fatherland, Denmark, and when I began to dread the shame of having to give up these studies, which I had cultivated with so much trouble and at such enormous cost and for so many years, in fact until the twenty-first year [i. e. December 1576—April 1597], which is known usually to be critical and apt to bring changes, I began to consider whether it would be possible to invent other astronomical instruments of less elaborate equipment, by means of which it would be possible to obtain, simply and accurately, results identical with those yielded by the others constructed in Denmark; instruments which could moreover be transported easily to any other place, in case it would not be possible to have those that I possessed in Denmark brought to me quickly and easily enough. Thus I am convinced that I have recently been able, by the grace of God, to invent some such instruments. Among them are three rulers for measuring not only, as did the Ptolemaic rulers, the altitudes of the stars, but also their angular distances, and which can easily be put together and transported to any place. We have also invented an armillary instrument, consisting of one and a half armillae [rings] only, with the aid of which not only declinations and right ascensions of the stars can be determined, but in addition, with the greatest ease, their longitudes and latitudes. With this same instrument one can further observe altitude and azimuth if it be correctly mounted for this purpose. In fact it will even prove suitable for measuring stellar distances if it be desired to put it to such a use. In this way this one instrument will be able to solve all these problems, and it will be possible to take it apart and put it together again without difficulty if desired. Packed in its box, and well protected, it can be transported to other places. I have also invented another method by which the same very advantageous and useful instrument might be simply constructed from some flat alidades joined together into a quadrangular or triangular form in such a way that it could perfectly well do all that was said of the previous instrument, and in addition several other things if desired. The latter instrument would also have the advantage in comparison with the previous one that it could be transported to other and yet other places with still greater ease, namely, when it is taken apart and arranged in such a way as to take up less room, and then packed into a longer oblong little box. It could moreover be confidently constructed to a greater size than the previous instrument. Finally I have invented another instrument which, with one single circle, is suitable for an ingenious determination of the declinations and right ascensions of the stars, their longitudes and latitudes, and in addition their angular distances, altitudes, and azimuths. It is possible to construct this instrument in a quadrangular form also, although this would not be as convenient. The same may even to a certain extent be obtained with a semicircle, or with a third, or a fourth of a circle, although not in such a simple way and all at once, but sometimes necessitating a combination of a number of observations. If these are carried out correctly however they will lead to the desired result with sufficient accuracy and certainty. I shall hardly publish anything about these and similar matters that I have invented hitherto, driven by necessity, the teacher of all sciences, nor about those that I shall invent in future, provided this same beneficent Deity be gracious to me. The reason is that I do not want such precious inventions to lose their value by being known to everybody, as often happens. To distinguished and princely persons however who might be especially interested in such matters, and likely to cultivate these sublime sciences with greater ardour than others and to further them in a liberal and laudable way, only to such persons shall I be willing to reveal and explain these matters when convinced of their gracious benevolence, but even then only on condition that they will not give them away.

14

GLOBUS MAGNUS ORICHALCICUS

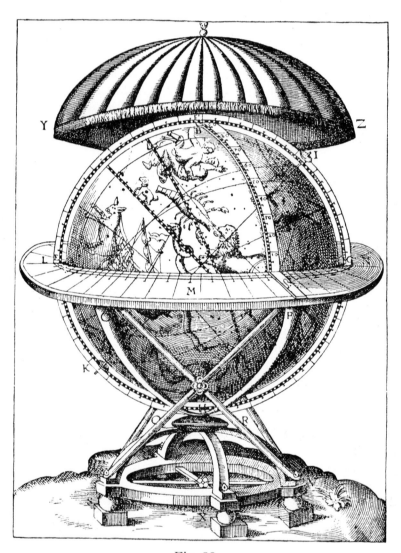

Fig. 22.

GLOBUS MAGNUS ORICHALCICUS

THE GREAT BRASS GLOBE

DESCRIPTION AND USE OF THE INSTRUMENT

We also had a very large globe made with great care, and at no small cost (which applies to all the other instruments as well). Inside it is built of wood, ingeniously put together from many rings and small pieces fitted together and on all sides having their support at the centre. The wood is then turned so that it becomes spherical in shape. When in 1570 in Augsburg, before I left for my fatherland, I had found a clever craftsman, a person I had long searched for in vain in other places, I had him make this as far as the wooden part was concerned. On account of its great size which made transport difficult it remained in Augsburg for five years. But when, in the year 1575, I returned to the place on my way home from Italy, at the time when His Majesty the Emperor Rudolph II was about to be crowned, and I was going to Regensburg by way of Augsburg I found this globe, made so long ago, and saw that it was not sufficiently rounded on all sides besides showing several cracks. Nevertheless I had it sent to me in Denmark the next year though not without difficulty. I then had its cracks filled, and its exactly spherical shape restored by inserting many hundred pieces of parchment. After that I tested it for two whole years, to see whether it would any where lose its shape and whether it could stand the temperature changes of two summers and two winters. When finally it was quite clear to me that it stayed completely spherical at every point, I did not hesitate to cover it all over with thin brass sheets of suitable thickness, and this was done with such great care and accuracy that one might believe the globe to be of solid brass, the joining of the sheets being hardly visible. Later I also had it smoothed so that its shape became exactly spherical. Finally we drew on it the zodiac and the equator with their poles, and then divided each degree of these circles accurately into 60 minutes of arc, by means of transversal points according to our custom. Before making the divisions however we let another year elapse in order to test whether the globe, after it had been covered with brass, would stay completely spherical throughout the winter as well as the summer. This having been sufficiently tested I placed the circles mentioned on it and also entered

14*

in their proper places those stars of the eighth sphere which I had meanwhile observed with the greatest care, determining their positions. Their number had been steadily increasing during the succeeding years and finally reached 1000, so that all the stars that are just visible to the eye were entered on the globe. The positions of the stars I purposely referred to the end of the year 1600, a year which would soon be commencing. Thus about 25 years elapsed from first beginning to make this globe until its completion, both as regards its divisions and its stars. Although this long interval of time may seem annoying, it has, nevertheless, been of no little advantage by making it possible to complete the whole work with so much the greater certainty, perfection, and accuracy. If it has been done well enough it has also been done quickly enough. Meanwhile the outer armillae were also mounted, namely the meridian, denoted by the letters EFGH [Fig. 22], and the horizon (about which more later), within which the whole globe is confined and turns about its axis through the poles IK. This meridian is made of strong steel, and it is provided with divisions by which all degrees are subdivided into their single minutes. The horizon LMN, the width of which is a span [cf. p. 9], is also covered with brass and divided into degrees and minutes in order to indicate the azimuth. A vertical quadrant of brass extends from the zenith to the horizon, beginning at B and ending at the horizon. It is divided into 90 degrees and their single minutes and it serves the double purpose of indicating altitudes by means of its own divisions, and also azimuths on the horizon. The entire horizon, together with its meridian as well as the whole globe enclosed by these rings, rest upon a strong base denoted by OPQRSTUX [should be OPQRSTVX] including two iron bars QR cutting each other cross-wise. They are visible on one side, but there are two similar bars behind. They serve for support and rigidity, so that the horizon and the whole instrument will not shift in the least on account of its size and weight. The entire support is about five feet high [130 cm, cf. p. 9], and on its lower part for the sake of decoration, are depicted various Astronomers and many other devices which one and all add to its beauty. The globe proper measures almost six feet in diameter [149 cm, cf. p. 9] and from this the size of the meridian, the horizon, and the rest, may be inferred. A globe of this size, so solidly and finely worked, and correct in every respect, has never I think been constructed up to now by any man anywhere in the world. (May I be forgiven if I boast). It is a huge and splendid piece of work. Many people from various countries travelled to Denmark in order to see this globe and my other instruments while the kingdom of Urania and the magnificent castle were still safe. Along the horizon one reads the following inscription in golden letters.

In the year of Our Lord 1584, when Frederick II ruled in Denmark, Tycho Brahe, Otto's son, had this globe made for himself and for his successors, in accordance with the mechanics of the heavens. It was his intention to represent exactly the stars fixed to the eighth sphere, each in its proper position, having observed them in the sky with his instruments, and with the help of these to investigate the appearances of the wandering stars, thus by a mechanical piece of work opening the sky to those of the inhabitants of the earth who are able to comprehend this system of reason.

The reason for giving the year as 1584 is, that this year was about the middle of the period during which this work was carried out, that is four years before King Frederick, of glorious memory, departed this life, he who generously and graciously supported me and my studies and followed them with Royal favour as long as he lived. It only remains to add that this magnificent instrument is provided with a cover, denoted by YZ, to put on top of it. This cover is hollow inside and round, and it comprises the upper hemisphere of the globe. It may be lowered if desired with the aid of a rope moving around a screw that is fastened to a beam, and thus protect the globe from dust and other forms of dirt.

The use of this globe is similar to that of other astronomical instruments. I intend to write about this in a special book, when I have the time, for it cannot be done in a few words. On account of its size, however, this globe has the advantage over others that everything can be carried out with the greatest accuracy, indeed even to a minute of arc. Thus it is possible to determine mechanically, with very little trouble and without difficult calculations, all the details concerning the doctrine of the diurnal rotation of the heavens as well as observations of the celestial bodies relative to the ecliptic and the equator, or any other celestial circles.

DE IIS QUÆ HACTENUS IN ASTRONOMICIS DEI
DONO, EXANTLAVIMUS, QUÆQUE POSTHAC EODEM FAVENTE,
EXEQUENDA RESTANT

ON THAT WHICH WE HAVE HITHERTO ACCOMPLISHED
IN ASTRONOMY WITH GOD'S HELP, AND ON THAT WHICH WITH HIS
GRACIOUS AID HAS YET TO BE COMPLETED IN THE FUTURE

In the year of Our Lord 1563, that is 35 years ago, on the occasion of the great conjunction of the upper planets which took place at the end of Cancer and the beginning of Leo, when I had reached the age of sixteen years, I was occupied with studies of classical literature in Leipzig, where I lived with my governor, supported by my beloved paternal uncle JØRGEN BRAHE, who died about 30 years ago. For my father, OTTO BRAHE, whom I recollect with deference, was not particularly anxious that his five sons, of whom I am the eldest, should learn Latin; later, however, he himself regretted this attitude. But from my earliest youth the uncle mentioned had brought me up, and thereafter he supported me generously during his lifetime until my eighteenth year; and he always treated me as his own son, and had decided to instate me as his heir. For his own marriage was childless; he was married to the noble and wise Mistress INGER OXE, a sister of the great PEDER OXE who later became chancellor of Denmark. She too, who died five years ago now as long as she lived regarded me with exceptional love, as if I were her own son. Later on she was for twelve years, during the reign of King FREDERICK II, of illustrious memory, in charge of the Queen's court, and was succeeded in this position for eight years by my most beloved and highly esteemed mother BEATE BILLE, who through the grace of God is still living in her 71st year. So it happened by a particular decree of Fate that, after my uncle mentioned above had without the knowledge of my parents taken me away with him while I was in my earliest youth, I was sent to the grammar-school in my seventh year, and later at the age of thirteen [should be fifteen] was sent to Leipzig, where I remained for three years, in order to continue my studies. The reason why I go that far back in time is that I want to make it clear how it came about that I, who had at first occupied myself with the liberal studies, later on turned to Astronomy, and also that I wish gratefully to revive the memory of my parents, who have been so kind to me. But—in order now to come to the point—after I had already in my fatherland Denmark, with the aid of a few books, particularly ephemerides, made myself acquainted with the elements of Astronomy, a subject for which I had a natural inclination, now in Leipzig I began to study Astronomy more and more. This I did in spite of the fact that my governor, who pleading the wishes of my parents wanted me to study law (which I actually did as far as my age allowed it), did not like it and opposed it. I bought the astronomical books secretly, and read them in secret in order that the governor should not become aware of it. By and by I got accustomed to distinguishing the constellations of the sky, and in the course of a month I learnt to know them all, in so far as they were located in that part of the sky which was visible there. For this purpose I made use of a small celestial globe, not greater than a fist, which I used to take with me in the evening without mentioning it to anybody. I learnt this by myself, without any guidance; in fact I never had the benefit of a teacher in Mathematics (Astronomy), otherwise I might have made quicker and better progress in these subjects. Soon my attention was drawn towards the motions of the planets. But when I noted their positions among the fixed stars with the help of lines drawn between them, I noticed already at that time, using only the small celestial globe, that their positions in the sky agreed neither with the Alphonsinian nor with the Copernican tables, although the agreement with the latter was better than with the former. After that I therefore noticed their positions with ever increasing attention, and I frequently made comparisons with the numbers in the Prutenic tables (for I had made myself acquainted with these also without any help). I no longer trusted the ephemerides, because I had realized that the ephemerides of Stadius, at that time the only ones that were founded on these numbers, were in many respects inaccurate and erroneous. Since, however, I had no instruments at my disposal, my governor having refused to let me get any, I first made use of a rather large pair of compasses as well as I could, placing the vertex close to my eye and directing one of the legs towards the planet to be observed and the other towards some fixed star near it. Sometimes I measured in the same way the mutual distances of two planets and determined (by a simple calculation) the ratio of their angular distance to the whole periphery of the circle. Although this method of observation was not very accurate, yet with its help I made so much progress that it became quite clear to me that both tables suffered from intolerable errors. This was amply apparent from the great conjunction of Saturn and Jupiter in the year 1563, which I mentioned in the beginning, and this was precisely the reason why it became my starting point. For the discrepancy was a whole month when comparison was made with the Alphonsine numbers, and even some days, if only a very few, on comparison with those of Copernicus. For his calculation does not deviate very much from the true motion in the sky in the case of these two planets. This is particularly so for Saturn, who according to my observations has never deviated more than half a degree, or two thirds of a degree at most, from Copernicus' table, while Jupiter at times shows a larger departure. Later on, in the year 1564, I secretly had a wooden astronomical radius made according to the direction of Gemma Frisius. This instrument was provided with an accurate division utilizing transversal points by Bartholomæus Scultetus, who at the time lived in Leipzig, and with whom I was on intimate terms on account of our mutual interests. Scultetus had been taught the principle of transversal points by his teacher Homelius. When I had got this radius, I eagerly set about making stellar observations whenever I enjoyed the benefit of a clear sky, and often I stayed awake the whole night through, while my governor slept and knew nothing about it; for I observed the stars through a skylight and entered the observations specially in a small book, which is still in my possession. Soon afterwards I noticed that angular distances, which by the radius had been found to be equal, and which with the help of a mathematical calculation of proportions had been converted into numbers, did not in every respect agree with each other. After I had found the cause of the error, I invented a table by which I could correct the defects of this radius. For at the time I had no opportunity of having a new one made, since my governor who held the purse strings, would not allow things of this kind to be made for me. Thus it happened that I made many observations with this radius while I lived in Leipzig, and also later after I had been called back to my fatherland. When I afterwards returned to Germany, I studied the stars as much as possible, first in Wittenberg, and then in Rostock. But in 1569 and the following year, when I lived in Augsburg, I very often observed the stars, not only with the very large quadrant, which I had made in the garden of the mayor outside the city (about which I have spoken above) [cf. p. 89], but also with another instrument, a wooden sextant that I invented there, and I entered my observations in a special book. I also did this industriously later on, after I had again returned to my fatherland, using another similar, though somewhat larger instrument, particularly when the strange new star, that flared up in 1572, made me give up my chemical investigations which occupied me very much after I had started them in Augsburg and which I continued until that time, and turn towards the study of the celestial phenomena. Having observed it industriously I described it, first in a small book, later conscientiously and thoroughly in a whole volume. In the course of time I had other and yet other astronomical instruments made, some of which I took with me when I travelled again all through Germany and part of Italy. Even on the journey I continued to observe the stars whenever possible. When at length I had returned to the fatherland about the time of my 28th year, I quietly made preparations for another and longer journey. For I had made up my mind to settle in the town of Basel or its surroundings, where I had been before with this purpose in mind. I intended there to lay the foundation of the revival of Astronomy. For I liked that neighbourhood better than other regions of Germany partly on account of its famous University and the excellent learned men who live there, partly because of the healthy climate and the agreeable living, and finally because Basel is located so to speak at the point where the three biggest countries in Europe, Italy, France and Germany, meet, so that it would be possible by correspondence to form friendships with distinguished and learned men in different places. In this way it would be possible to make my inventions more widely known so that they might become more generally useful. I also had the feeling that it would not be sufficiently easy and convenient for me to pursue these studies in the fatherland, particularly if I stayed in Scania and on my property Knudstrup, or in some other greater province of Denmark where a continuous stream of noblemen and friends would disturb the scientific work and impede this kind of study. But it so happened that while I was inwardly contemplating these matters and was already making preparations for the journey, without however revealing my purpose, the noble and mighty Frederick II, King of Denmark and Norway, of illustrious memory, sent one of his young noblemen to me at Knudstrup with a Royal letter bidding me to go to see him immediately wherever he might be dwelling on Sealand. When I had presented myself without delay this excellent King, who cannot be sufficiently praised, of his own accord and according to his most gracious will offered me that island in the far-famed Danish Sound that our countrymen call Hven, but which is usually called Venusia in Latin, and Scarlatina by foreigners. He asked me to erect buildings on this island, and to construct instruments for astronomical investigations as well as for chemical studies, and he graciously promised me that he would abundantly defray the expenses. After I had for some time contemplated the matter and asked some wise men for their advice, I gave up my previous plan and willingly agreed to the King's wish, particularly when I saw that on this island, which is situated all by itself between Scania and Sealand, I could be rid of the disturbances of visitors, and that I could in this way obtain, in my own fatherland to which above other countries I owe so very much, the quiet and the convenient conditions that I had been looking for elsewhere. So, in the year 1576, I began building the castle Uraniborg, suitable for the study of Astronomy, and in the course of time I constructed buildings as well as astronomical instruments of various kinds, fitted for making accurate observations. The most important of these are delineated and explained in this book. Meanwhile I also energetically started observing, and for this work I made use of the assistance of several students who distinguished themselves by talents and a keen vision. I had such students in my house all the time, one class after another, and I taught them this and other sciences. Thus by the grace of God it came about that there was hardly any day or night with clear weather that we did not get a great many, and very accurate, astronomical observations of the fixed stars as well as of all the planets, and also of the comets that appeared during that time, seven of which were carefully observed in the sky from that place. In this way observations were industriously made during 21 years. These I first collected in some big volumes, but later on I divided them up and distributed them among single books, one for each year, and had fair copies made. The arrangement I followed was such that the fixed stars, in so far as they had been observed during the year in question, had their own place, while the planets all had theirs, first the sun and moon, and next the other five planets in order up to Mercury; for I observed this planet also, although it is very seldom visible. In fact we observed it carefully almost every year, in the morning as well as in the evening. And yet the great Copernicus cites as an excuse for his not having observed it the far too high latitude and the mists of the river Vistula. We however, at a still higher latitude and on an island surrounded on all sides by a misty sea, have seen it many times, as I said, and determined its position. But perhaps the house where Copernicus lived was not located in such a way that the horizon was free in all directions, and therefore was not quite suitable for making observations, especially at such a low altitude. This I have also heard from the one among my collaborators whom I sent there 14 years ago to investigate the altitude of the pole [cf. p. 45]. Since Copernicus did not therefore have observations of his own of Mercury to build on, he was obliged to borrow some from a volume of observations by Walter, a pupil of Regiomontanus and a citizen of Nürnberg; and although he has not made them the foundation of his opinions and demonstration with any high degree of care and accuracy, one might still have wished that in the case of the other planets, the orbits of which he tried to determine with immense audacity using his own observations, he had not procured some that were still more uncertain. For then we should know by now their apogees and eccentricities, and the other quantities of this kind, much more accurately, and it would have saved me many years of immense and untiring work and enormous expense. Being now in possession of the selected and careful observations of 21 years, made in the sky with different ingeniously constructed instruments that I have shown in the preceding pages (not to speak of the observations of the previous 14 years), I hold them as a very rare and costly treasure. Perhaps I shall at some time publish all of them, if God in his grace will permit me to add still more.

All this shows that I have observed the stars continuously from my sixteenth year, and that I have continued these observations for nearly 35 years, up to the present day; yet they were not all of equal accuracy and importance. For those that I made in Leipzig in my youth and up to my 21st year, I usually call childish and of doubtful value. Those that I took later until my 28th year I call juvenile and fairly serviceable. The third group however, which I made at Uraniborg during approximately the last 21 years with the greatest care and with very accurate instruments at a more mature age, until I was fifty years of age, those I call the observations of my manhood, completely valid and absolutely certain, and this is my opinion of them. It is particularly upon these observations that I build when I strive by energetic labours to lay the foundations of and develop a renewed Astronomy, although some of the observations of the previous years contribute considerably. But that which I have hitherto carried out and prepared in this field with God's help and that which I have yet, with the help of the same gracious God, to do and bring to a conclusion during days to come, I shall now describe.

First of all we determined the course of the sun by very careful observations during several years. We not only investigated with great care its entrance into the equinoctial points, but we also considered the positions lying in between these and the solstitial points, particularly in the northern semicircle of the ecliptic since the sun there is not affected by refraction at noon. Observations were made in both cases and repeatedly confirmed, and from these I calculated mathematically both the apogee and the eccentricity corresponding to these times. With regard to the apogee as well as the eccentricity an obvious error has crept into both the Alphonsine tables and Copernicus' work, so that the apogee of the sun is almost three degrees ahead of Copernicus' value. The eccentricity amounts to about $2^1/_6$ when the radius of the eccentric orbit is put equal to 60, while the value of Copernicus is too small by almost a quarter [Copernicus' value of the eccentricity is 0.0323, or 1.938 when the radius of the eccentric orbit is put equal to 60. The corresponding maximum inequality of the longitude is 1°51′. Tycho Brahe's values of these quantities are 0.0359, 2.156, and 2°3′]. He also commits an error in the determination of the sun's motus simplex during these years which amounts to about a quarter of a degree. From this the Alphonsine determinations may be judged comparing them with those of Copernicus. From these data I derived the rules of the sun's uniform motion, as well as those of its prostaphaeresis [inequality] and established them by accurate values. As a consequence there can no longer be any doubt that the orbit of the sun is accurately determined and explained by suitable numbers. This work on the sun was of necessity the first thing that had to be done, since it is on the sun that the motions of the celestial bodies depend, and since it moves in the ecliptic, to which the other motions are referred. I also determined the obliquity of the ecliptic relative to the equator and found a value differing from that of Copernicus and his contemporaries, namely 23 degrees and $31^1/_2$ minutes, that is $3^1/_2$ minutes greater than the value they found. I took the refraction of the sun in its winter position into account, a quantity which they had thoughtlessly overlooked. We also provided tables for the various revolutions of the sun, and we also added tables of declinations and right ascensions, based on our observations. We furthermore took its parallax and refraction into account, by means of special tables.

With regard to the m o o n we used no less diligence in order to explain its intricate path, which in so many ways is complicated and not so simple and easy to make out as the ancients and Copernicus thought. For it presents another inequality with regard to the longitude, which these astronomers did not notice; nor have they determined the ratios of its revolution with sufficient accuracy. Moreover the limits of its maximum latitude differ from the value determined by Ptolemy, who with regard to this point was too confidently followed by all subsequent astronomers. In fact, this inequality of the moon even varies in a non-uniform way, the deviations amounting to a third of a degree. Nor are the nodes, which are the points of intersection of its orbit and the ecliptic, moving uniformly as was previously assumed; every revolution of the moon in its orbit makes them move to and fro, and the difference is quite considerable, amounting on both sides to somewhat more than one and a half degrees. This is all apparent from our most careful observations and calculations, among which are some pertaining to 18 eclipses of the moon that were accurately observed by us. For three lunar eclipses are not sufficient for the study of the first inequality as Ptolemy, Albategnius and Copernicus thought. In addition six solar eclipses were employed, in so far as they could contribute to the purpose. Further the moon was investigated in its quadratures, and at the greatest elongation from its mean motion, near the apogee as well as near the perigee, and also at the intermediate points. This was done in many ways and very often in order that its intricate course might be properly determined, and it has caused us many years of incredible effort. Finally, however, we found methods by which it was possible to make its non-uniform and multifarious wanderings subject to rules expressed by circles and numbers. Therefore, having established a new hypothesis that was in agreement with the phenomena [i. e. the observations], we adjusted the numbers representing the uniform as well as the non-uniform motions, not only in longitude, but also in latitude, and we took account of its parallax by a method differing from that of Ptolemy and Copernicus, but which agreed with experience, and also with the hypothesis itself. We also took account of the moon's refraction, since it is impossible without this accurately to distinguish the rest. All this and several other relations regarding the moon we put into concise tables, the purpose being the derivation, by calculation, of the motions thereby described. [An account of Tycho Brahe's theory of the motion of the moon is given in Dreyer, Planetary Systems, p. 368]. After the orbits of both celestial bodies [the sun and the moon] have thus been determined in such a way that they agree with the celestial phenomena, it follows that it will be possible to determine with absolute correctness their eclipses, their relative positions, and their motions and places, the need for which has been long felt. What we have said so far about the course of the sun and the moon, and the question of agreement with celestial phenomena, is clearly presented together with other subjects, in the first chapter of our *Astronomiae instauratae Progymnasmata* [Opera Omnia II, p. 13 f.]. Anybody interested in the subject will there find what he wants. With regard to the further investigation of these celestial bodies, the only thing that is still lacking is an adjustment valid for many centuries, and a presentation in greater generality. This would not involve a very great effort, if only the observations of the ancients and of our predecessors, on which the investigation would have to be based, could be trusted. This full and comprehensive account we reserve for our work *Theatrum Astronomicum*. For the present anybody interested in Astronomy, will benefit by reading our exposition in the part of the *Progymnasmata* referred to above, and there he will find what he wants.

Further, as far as time and circumstances permitted, we very carefully determined the positions of all fixed stars visible to the naked eye, even those that are denoted as stars of the sixth magnitude, the longitude as well as the latitude. The accuracy was one minute of arc, in some cases even half a minute of arc. In this way we determined the positions of one thousand stars. The ancients were only able to count 22 more in spite of the fact that they lived at a lower geographical latitude where they ought to be able to see as many more as would correspond to the 200 stars that are always hidden from us here. Instead of these we determined a number of others which are very small, and which they did not include on this account. This immense task occupied us for almost 20 years, as we wished to investigate the whole problem carefully with different instruments. Since however the very small stars are only visible during the winter, when the nights are sufficiently dark, and even then only when the moon is not in the sky, it took many years of patient work before this task was fully completed in a satisfactory way. Add to this that at the time of the new moon, when this work is best carried out, the sky was seldom clear. The method we used for the accurate determination of the longitudes of the fixed stars from the equinoctial point is set forth sufficiently clearly in the second chapter of the *Progymnasmata* mentioned [Opera Omnia II, p. 159 f.]. It consists in using Venus, both as a morning star and as an evening star, as a connecting link between the sun and the fixed stars. The connection is carried out with several stars and these are all referred to the brightest star above the head of the Ram, which is denoted as the third [*a* Arietis]. (We preferred this star to the others, because the two preceding stars are fainter). From the exposition in the *Progymnasmata* it will also be clear how we determined the positions of the others relative to this star, and in particular how we used a triple procedure comprising certain selected stars located along the zodiac and the equator all around the sky, and succeeded in making the intervals accurately fill the entire circumference [cf. Opera Omnia II, p. 198 f.]. I have also noticed that the irregularity of the rate of change of their longitudes [trepidation] is not so considerable as Copernicus assumed. His erroneous ideas on this matter are a consequence of the incorrect observations of the ancients, as well as those of more recent times. Consequently the precession of the equinoctial point during these years is not so slow as he asserted. For in our times the fixed stars do not take a hundred years to move one degree, as indicated in his table, but only $71^1/_2$ years. This has practically always been the case, as appears when the observations of our predecessors are carefully checked. In fact only a small irregularity appears, which is due to accidental causes. This we shall, God willing, explain in more detail in due course.

The fact that the latitudes of the fixed stars are also undergoing changes as a consequence of the change in the obliquity of the ecliptic, was first discovered by me. In the chapter mentioned above I have proved it by various examples. Thus we can maintain with ample certainty, and this is confirmed by actual experience, that the positions of the fixed stars have been determined by us with perfect and infallible accuracy. We have even determined a great many of them several times, and with different instruments, too, each leading to the same result. We have not in carrying out this work made use of mechanical devices, although the great brass globe was at our disposal, but every star has been assigned its proper position by cumbersome trigonometrical calculations. This will already be clear from what has been said towards the end of the chapter mentioned on the subject of the constellation of Cassiopeia (in which we count 26 stars, twice as many as the ancients), but for other, and yet other stars we have developed the trigonometrical measurements and calculations even further, when it appeared expedient. Had the ancients and our predecessors spent as much labour in determining the positions of the stars, their catalogue, handed down to us from the time of Hipparchus, would not have been so full of errors. In fact it is not even correct within a sixth of a degree—that being the accuracy to which the positions are given—but contains far greater errors, often quite intolerable. In order to see this clearly it suffices to consider the angular distances between the stars, which remain for ever the same. For a great number of stars there is a considerable deviation from what is required by the values of the ancients. That all fixed stars always keep their relative positions is, however, made sufficiently clear by the stars which according to Hipparchus and Ptolemy are in a straight line; for this is still the case without any change. We shall in due course present a catalogue of all the stars for which we determined longitudes and latitudes with an accuracy of a minute of arc, or in certain cases, as already mentioned, of half a minute of arc.

We have not only striven to determine carefully longitudes and latitudes of the fixed stars, but for some particularly important stars, 100 altogether, we have also by trigonometrical calculation derived the right ascensions and declinations, and referred these to two secular years (namely 1600 and 1700), so that it is possible by a proportional calculation to derive values valid for epochs in between. The refraction of the stars can be taken into account with the help of a special table that has been prepared on the basis of long and multitudinous experiments. For if refraction be neglected, it is not possible to derive accurate positions of the fixed stars, particularly when they are near the horizon at an altitude of less than twenty degrees. Therefore it was always our custom to take the error of refraction into account whenever it was necessary for determining the improved position of the stars. This refraction in the case of the fixed stars differs slightly from that of the sun (let me here make this statement also). It also differs somewhat from that valid for the moon, as was disclosed and explained by us a long time ago.

The only thing which is yet wanting with regard to the stars is to indicate their general motion through all the centuries during which the world has existed. It would not be so difficult to do this carefully, had the observations of the ancients in this field not been accepted, as they actually were. Yet I am convinced that I shall, by suitable corrections, be able to satisfy astronomers in this respect also, as far as that is possible.

One might have wished that the other stars which were catalogued by the ancients, but which are invisible in our latitudes, could have been added to the first thousand that I determined. Further, there are all the others, which were invisible even to the ancients who lived in the regions of Egypt, namely those that are located around the south pole of the sky. For from the narratives of people who have sailed across the equator we know that there, too, the most beautiful stars are shining. With regard to the first proposition, it would be necessary to go to Egypt or some other similar place in Africa, and there industriously to note all the stars visible from that part of the world. But in order to attain the second goal it would be necessary to sail to South America, or to some other country beyond the equator, whence all the stars around the southern pole are visible, and observe them from there. So, if some mighty noblemen would care to fulfil our own and others' wishes in both these respects, they would do a very good deed that would be ever gloriously remembered. Up to now no one has even tried to do a thing like this in the right way, let alone carried it out, as far as is known. I would be willing to provide the necessary instruments and tools if somebody could organize the work and get the right people for such a deserving enterprise.

With regard finally to the investigations of the intricate course of the five other planets, and attempts at explaining them, I have done all I could. For in this whole field we have assembled, first of all, the apogees as well as the eccentricities, and further the angular motions and the ratios of their orbits and periods, so that they no longer contain all the numerous errors of previous investigations. We have shown that the very apogees of the planets are subject to yet another inequality that had not previously been noted. Further, we have made the discovery that the annual period, which Copernicus explained by a motion of the earth in a large circle, while the ancients explained it by epicycles, is subject to a variation. All this and other matters connected with it we have remedied by means of a special hypothesis [the Tychonic System] that we invented and worked out 14 years ago, basing it on the phenomena. There are certain persons, of whom I know three with distinguished names, who have not been ashamed to appropriate this hypothesis and present it as their own invention. In due course I shall, God willing, point out the occasions on which they did it, and repudiate and refute their immense impudence, and I shall demonstrate that the fact of the matter is as I say, and that so clearly that it will be impossible for impartial men to doubt or contradict me. But if they honestly admit their error, and give that back to me which is mine, then I shall bear with them, and therefore I now willingly refrain from mentioning their names. [Reymers, Liddel, and Röslin].

Nor have we left the latitudes unchanged, but revised the results given by our predecessors from Ptolemy onwards. For the five planets we carefully noted the latitudes during the whole of the revolution, and from these observations we determined revised values of the maximum latitudes and of their transits over the ecliptic, in such a way that everything was in accordance with the sky. Hereby we made the clear observation that the nodes and the maximum latitudes of the three upper planets do not depend in a regular way on the motions of their apogees, but have a special motion, at any rate if it can be assumed that the results of Ptolemy regarding this subject are correct, those which both the Alphonsine tables and Copernicus use without any correction by observations of their own. As a consequence it may happen that the planets have a southern latitude in the sky, while the tables indicate a northern latitude, or vice versa. [Cf. Opera Omnia V, p. 254 f.].

With regard to all five planets there remains only one thing to do, namely to construct new and correct tables expressing by numbers all that has been established by more than 25 years of careful celestial observations (without mentioning the observations of the previous 10 years), thereby demonstrating the inaccuracy of the usual tables. We began this work and laid its foundations. It will not be difficult to complete it with the help of a few computers, and the results will then serve as a basis for the calculation of ephemerides for the coming years, as many as desired. The same can be done for the sun and the moon, for which we already have tables. In this way it will be possible with the greatest ease to demonstrate to posterity that the course of the celestial bodies as determined by us agrees with the phenomena, and is correctly given in every respect.

Finally it would be of great importance to the perfection of Astronomy in all directions, if it were possible to determine correctly not only geographical latitudes, but also geographical longitudes of localities on the earth. We investigated this problem industriously as far as this was possible, and we are convinced that we made determinations for various places that are more nearly correct than the previous ones. However, it is impossible to attend to this problem without having recourse to observations of the times of several lunar eclipses made with equal accuracy in various widely separated localities by different observers. Therefore, as before, if kings and princes and other mighty noblemen in widely separated parts of the world would generously make suitable preparations, then they would really be doing a good deed, and in this way Astronomy, which is in need of widely different terrestrial horizons, would develop towards greater perfection.

While we thus with untiring industry through many years observed these eternal celestial bodies which are as old as the world itself, we studied with equal care all new celestial bodies in the ethereal regions that appeared during this time, above all the new and very admirable star that was first seen towards the end of the year 1572 and stayed for 16 months before it became completely invisible. On the subject of this star we wrote a small book describing its appearance, while it was still visible, as I have already indicated. When we resumed this work a few years later, we prepared a whole volume on this same star on account of the wonderful nature of the phenomenon, and we found it suitable to incorporate it in the first volume of the *Progymnasmata* for certain reasons that are indicated there [Opera Omnia II, pp. 305—435 and III, pp. 1—319]. In this volume I am not content to present clearly our own observations with regard to this marvellous star, and to elucidate them geometrically, but I discuss, too, the opinions of others about the same star, in so far as it was possible for me to get them and become acquainted with them. This I do with scientific liberty, examining them and making it clear whether they were in accordance with the truth, or not.

We also prepared a special book on the immense comet that appeared five years later [Opera Omnia IV, pp. 1—378]. In this we discuss it fully, including in the discussion our own observations and determinations as well as the opinions of others. We add a few pamphlets on this same subject, which elucidate this cometary problem more fully, and it was our plan to include all this in the first part of the second volume of the *Progymnasmata*. In the second part we shall, God willing, deal with the remaining six smaller comets that we observed with equal care in some of the subsequent years. Although all this has not yet been quite completed, the more important parts, and most of the demonstration, has been prepared. For the constant stars have not left us with sufficient time to dwell too long on these fading and quickly passing celestial bodies. Yet I hope that I shall soon, with the help of the gracious God, complete the second part of the second volume also. In this volume I shall clearly demonstrate that all the comets observed by me moved in the ethereal regions of the world and never in the air below the moon as Aristotle and his followers have tried without reason to make us believe for so many centuries; and the demonstration will be clearest for some of the comets, while for others it will be according to the opportunity I had. The reason why I treat the comets in the second volume of the *Progymnasmata* before I set about the other five planets, which I intend to discuss in the third volume, are given in the same place in the preface [Opera Omnia IV, pp. 6—8]. But the principal reason is that the results pertaining to the comets, the true ethereal nature of which I prove conclusively, show that the entire sky is transparent and clear, and cannot contain any solid and real spheres. For the comets as a rule follow orbits of a kind that no celestial sphere whatever would permit, and consequently it is a settled thing that there is nothing unreasonable in the hypothesis invented by us [the Tychonic System], since we have found that there is no such thing as penetration of spheres and limits of distance, as the solid spheres do not really exist.

With regard to that which we have until now accomplished in Astronomy, and to that which has yet to be done, this brief account must now suffice.

In the field of Astrology, too, we carried out work that should not be looked down upon by those who study the influences of the stars. Our purpose was to rid this field of mistakes and superstition, and to obtain the best possible agreement with the experience on which it is based. For I think that it will hardly be possible to find in this field a perfectly accurate theory that can come up to mathematical and astronomical truth. Having in my youth been more interested in this foretelling part of Astronomy that deals with prophesying and builds on conjectures, I later on, feeling that the courses of the stars upon which it builds were insufficiently known, put it aside until I should have remedied this want. After I at length obtained more accurate knowledge of the orbits of the celestial bodies, I took Astrology up again from time to time, and I arrived at the conclusion that this science, although it is considered idle and meaningless not only by laymen but also by most scholars, among which are even several astronomers, is really more reliable than one would think; and this is true not only with regard to meteorological influences and predictions of the weather [natural astrology], but also concerning the predictions by nativities [judicial astrology], provided that the times are determined correctly, and that the courses of the stars and their entrances into definite sections of the sky are utilized in accordance with the actual sky, and that their directions of motion and revolutions are correctly worked up. With regard to these two points we have developed a method, based on experience, which differs from those used up to now. But we are not inclined to

118

communicate this kind of astrological knowledge to others, since not a little has
been made out by us in this field. For it is not given to everybody to know how to
use it on their own, without superstition or excessive confidence, which it is not wise
to show towards created things. Therefore we shall not publish any, or at least very
little, of the things that we have found out in this field. What I have now briefly and
in all generality stated here about the subject in question, must therefore suffice.

I also made with much care alchemical investigations, or chemical experiments.
This subject too, I shall occasionally mention here, as the substances treated are
somewhat analogous to the celestial bodies and their influences, for which reason
I usually call this science terrestrial Astronomy. I have been occupied by this subject
as much as by the celestial studies from my 23rd year, trying to gain knowledge and
to prepare it, and up to now I have with much labour and at great expense made a
great many findings with regard to the metals and minerals as well as the precious
stones and plants, and other similar substances. I shall be willing to discuss these
questions frankly with princes and noblemen, and other distinguished and learned
people, who are interested in this subject and know something about it, and I shall
occasionally give them information, as long as I feel sure of their good intentions
and that they will keep it secret. For it serves no useful purpose, and is unreasonable,
to make such things generally known. For although many people pretend to understand them, it is not given to everybody to treat these mysteries properly according
to the demands of nature, and in an honest and beneficial way.

APPENDIX

DE ARCHITECTONICIS STRUCTURIS ASTRO-NOMICIS OBSERVATIONIBUS ACCOMMODIS

ON ARCHITECTONIC STRUCTURES SUITABLE FOR ASTRONOMICAL OBSERVATIONS

The description of astronomical instruments given above in such a manner as I found expedient, more than sufficiently treat the mechanical part of the art, which ought to precede everything else, and without which it is no use entering on the rest, and by their not only pleasant, but also useful and almost necessary variety and abundance they serve all kinds of purposes completely. But if these instruments should be able properly and without difficulty to serve the purpose for which they are intended, not only a place is required, but also proper buildings, where it is possible without difficulty or disturbance of any kind to do this work. First of all, the place should be in a high locality from where there is a free view round the whole horizon, without woods or mountains or other buildings intervening. It is also preferable that it is a solitary place, free from the commotion of the common herd, where it is possible to enjoy philosophical tranquillity, although so that the things needed are available and learned and intelligent persons can frequently be admitted, while the common herd, which is no judge of such things or does not attribute to them the value they deserve, can be excluded. And even though the more southerly regions, where the orbits of the stars stand more vertically on the horizon and the heavens are more frequently bright, might be thought preferable to those closer to the poles and more northerly or arctic as in my country, it is not opportune for everybody for that reason to leave his native country or the place where he lives, and perhaps he cannot either, in all more southerly regions of the earth, particularly in unknown and foreign countries, succeed in finding the conditions and facilities needed, and so he must content himself with the conditions of place and time offered to him and which he may obtain, and with constant care try to surmount the existing difficulties and inconveniences, in order that things should not turn out as said by Seneca of Time: "We have not enough of it, but we waste much of it." It is true that in Egypt and other regions of Africa and Asia, where the ancient astronomers lived, it was easier to get an opportunity for such works, because the heavens are said to be brighter there and the orbits of the stars have a steeper inclination; but as Bellona under the reign of the Turks has driven away nearly all free sciences from there, it is only natural that Astronomy should be in exile, too, or be held in less esteem in these countries, except in so far as it is perhaps in a certain way cultivated by the Arabs. As to other regions of Europe situated in the south, we might at any rate cherish greater hopes in so far as they are not ruled by the Turks or the Muscovites, as they do not there disdain the free sciences, but, as also most of these countries are occupied by others, and, to my knowledge, are less interested in Astronomy, one would probably do more harm than good, if one preferred these regions, however far south they are situated, to those farther north. On the contrary, as in winter, when nights are longer, it is possible to make observations more easily and on a larger scale, the northern regions have the advantage that they do not only offer this opportunity, but further, because of their sharp cold, particularly at a north wind, purify and rarefy the air to such a degree that it is often perfectly clean for several days running, so that the stars shine and twinkle at night to the highest degree, while at that time it is often raining in the more southerly regions, or the heavens at other times are over-clouded and moist and less accessible to the observation of the celestial bodies. It is true that Prince Wilhelm, Landgrave of Hesse, etc., of glorious memory, who was highly interested in Astronomy, and was not a little initiated into it, encouraged me to settle in a more southerly place on earth in order to be able to watch the celestial bodies on a larger scale, as appears from a letter from him to me printed in the first volume of my astronomical letters p. 21 [Opera Omnia VI, p. 48—49]. And there is no doubt that he did so with the best intentions, and perhaps also to entice me to go there. But I am of opinion that no fewer observations can be made in Denmark than in Hesse or any other part of Germany, to say nothing of other European countries, apart from the fact that in the more southerly regions some stars appear which are always hidden in the north. This is not, however, of particular importance and does not contribute very much to the redintegration of astronomy. This may be proved from the twenty-one manuscript books in my possession, which contain very accurate observations from as many years, all made in Denmark, so many and so good as I think nobody has hitherto provided in other places, even in more southerly regions,— may my words not give offence! Here are found not only frequent and multitudinous investigations of all the places of the planets and their changing courses for each single year, even of Mercury, which appears more rarely as it retires very little from the sun; but also the positions of the fixed stars, in so far as they are in any way visible, have been recorded and on the basis of the notes entered in a catalogue of such a kind that it is impossible to find anybody, even among those who formerly lived in Egypt and the southern countries and the regions where the air is considered serener, who has performed anything like it, any more than any of their successors wherever they may be. I shall, God willing, soon prove that I do not tell all this out of arrogance or in contempt of the ancients in any way, but because I am in harmony with the truth.

So much for the choice of place, at which, however, I permit anybody to follow his own taste as he likes. Circumstances will offer other suggestions, and even if it is impossible to have all one's wishes fulfilled, one must accept the facilities that offer themselves, so that one rather obtains something than nothing.

Further, the buildings ought to be so constructed that they may conveniently serve the observations and yield space for all the various instruments so that in accordance with their size and form they may be placed in a fixed position and in the right and proper manner. Further they should be protected against being damaged by the air, wind, and rain. Likewise, they must above the instruments themselves be provided with a roof, which, when necessary, can easily be opened and again closed. The material of which they are to be built, must be all stone, either bricks or other stones found in the soil, and if necessary the instruments must also, for the sake of safety, be supported by marble pillars or other stone pillars, and all must rest firmly on their base so that they cannot in any way shift, or in time come to rest less firmly. But the roof must be made of a more loosely joined material in order that it may be more easily opened and again closed. There must also be guardrooms and heating installations for those who are to assist these observers. And both this and the rest of the accessories ought to be arranged so practically that no trouble, no difficulty, and no inconvenience delays the work proper or makes it unpleasant.

But anybody who has the means, will at his discretion be able to devise and construct other forms of buildings for the purpose according to the opportunities of the place and the arrangement and number of the instruments. In this respect I am of opinion that I need not offer particular directions for anybody. But if anybody wants to know the procedure we have preferred and carried through in these building works, which have cost us so much trouble and so great expenditure, on this island of Venusia (in the vernacular called Hven) in the Danish Sound, which is visited by so many ships (a work which was begun twenty-two years ago), I shall state it in order that the places and the arrangement of the buildings may be known in which the instruments depicted and described above have been erected. Anybody may take what he wants from this account and adapt it according to his needs. For I hope that also in future there will be some who are caught by such high interests and who will take great pains to imitate or even surpass these works.

ARCIS URANIBURGI, QUO AD TOTAM
CAPACITATEM DESIGNATIO

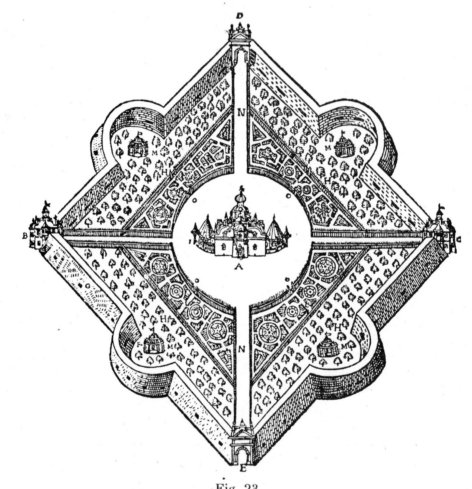

Fig. 23.

is possible, and in so far as I can in any way depict such things in a plane. For an enumeration of all the works carried out here, not only underground, but also what can be seen from the outside, although it is nearly incredible that this house will contain such heterogeneous things, would be too prolix, and, indeed, there might be those who would find it tedious.

You house dedicated to Urania, renowned beacon, erected in a high place and fortified with walls, surrounded by trees and lawns in your gardens, you, who in three times seven years have investigated all stars, while lifting your majestic head towards the Olymp—do you now stand unheeded? Do you stand silently and have been deserted? Perhaps it was so decided by the High Powers watching god-inspired thoughts. In order that the great tasks shall not be confined within narrow barriers they stir up everything earthly and have it changed in every manner. Glory be to you alone who governs the rotation of the heavens and the stars.

ORTHOGRAPHIA PRÆCIPUÆ DOMUS
ARCIS URANIBURGI IN INSULA PORTHMI DANICI VENUSIA VULGO HVENNA, ASTRONOMIÆ INSTAURANDÆ GRATIA CIRCA ANNUM 1580 A TYCHONE BRAHE EXÆDIFICATÆ

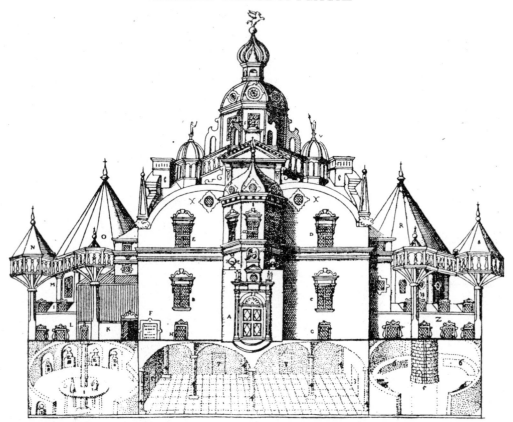

Fig. 24.

ICHNOGRAPHIA ET EIUS EXPLICATIO

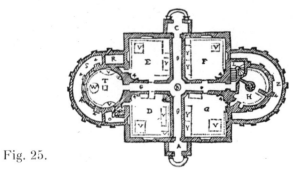

Fig. 25.

ORTHOGRAPHIA PRÆCIPUÆ DOMUS ARCIS

URANIBURGI IN INSULA PORTHMI DANICI VENUSIA VULGO
HVENNA, ASTRONOMIÆ INSTAURANDÆ GRATIA CIRCA ANNUM
1580 A TYCHONE BRAHE EXÆDIFICATÆ

DESIGN OF THE MAIN BUILDING OF URANIBORG ON

THE ISLAND OF VENUSIA, IN DANISH HVEN, IN THE DANISH SOUND,
BUILT FOR THE REDINTEGRATION OF ASTRONOMY BY TYCHO BRAHE
ABOUT THE YEAR 1580

GROUND-PLAN WITH EXPLANATION

A. The eastern door. C. The western door. Θ. Four corridors, which meet at right angles; later, however, they were reduced to three, in order that the winter dining-room or the heating installation D might be expanded, and that in one of its corners, behind the furnace, there might be a small hidden chemical laboratory, in which, however, five furnaces were placed apart, which might be more quickly at disposal for the chemical work there, in order that it should not always be necessary to go down into the larger room. B. A fountain provided with a water-carrying figure, which turned round and threw the water into the air in all directions when this was wanted. D. The winter dining-room mentioned. E. F. G. Spare bedrooms. L. Stairs leading to the upper floor. H. Kitchen. K. A built-up well, forty ells deep, which served a pumping-apparatus and, through pipes stretching in all directions, hidden in the walls, distributed the water to the various rooms, both in the upper and the lower storey. P. Stairs leading down to the chemical laboratory. T. Library. W. The large brass globe depicted sub no. 22 [cf. p. 103]. V. Four tables for the collaborators. 4. Chimneys leading from the lower laboratory and filling the corners of the four rooms. Y. Beds in these rooms, put in various places. The rest is easily understood by an acute reader. But all this must be imagined as being of such dimensions as to correspond to the base of the larger house depicted above, although in order to take up less space it is represented in about half the scale.

17

DESCRIPTION OF THE VARIOUS PARTS OF THE LARGE MAIN BUILDING

The erection of the large main building of Uraniborg was begun by me in the year 1576. Its foundation stone was laid by the Right Honourable Mr. CHARLES DANÇAY, for many years Envoy to Denmark of the Most Serene and Potent King of France, a man who, as regards integrity, skill, and practical experience was second to none and who further was closely familiar with the free sciences and finally, as long as he was alive (for he died eight years ago in his eighty-first year), constantly regarded me with a singular love and always to the greatest extent looked after me and my affairs. As soon as he learnt that this house was to be built, he offered of his own accord to lay the first corner-stone there, and later he had the following inscription carved on a porphyry stone:

When Frederick II reigned in Denmark, Charles Dançay, the Aquitanian, Envoy to Denmark of the King of France, in this house, which in accordance with the King's will was built by Tycho Brahe, the Nobleman, of Knudstrup to serve science, and particularly the study of the stars, had this votive stone laid down, which is to serve as a memorial and be a happy omen. In the year 1576, 8th of August.

When the day approached determined for the laying of the foundation-stone, the Excellent Dançay arrived, accompanied by several noblemen besides by some learned men among our common friends to attend this performance, and on the 8th of August in the morning, when the rising sun together with Jupiter was in the heart of Leo, while the moon was in the western heavens in Aquarius, he laid this stone in the presence of all of us, having first consecrated it with wine of various kinds and praying for good fortune in every respect, in which he was joined by the surrounding friends. This stone was laid in the eastern corner of the house towards the south-east, as denoted in the above picture by the letter F. Then the building of the whole house was commenced and after some years it was finished, although in the meantime not a few or insignificant difficulties and delays occurred, which are not worth being mentioned any more. But the design of the house added here is explained as follows: A. The eastern door, executed according to the Ionic and Doric orders. B. The winter dining-room. F. The mentioned foundation-stone, which was laid by the above-mentioned French Envoy. G and H. Basement windows. C. Spare bedroom; facing the west there are two similar rooms. M. Study and library. L. Subterranean, round chemical laboratory, containing sixteen different furnaces for chemical use. I. Aperture through which coals are shot for use in the chemical works. Z. Wood cellar. q. Kitchen. D. Chamber called the red one. a. A yellow octagonal chamber. E. The blue chamber. Facing the west and corresponding to these there is a larger summer dining-room painted green, the ceiling of which is decorated with paintings of the principal plants. From here it is possible, particularly in summer, to enjoy the view of a large number of ships passing. X. Windows in the upper storey. O. The larger, southern observatory containing several of the large and important astronomical instruments, particularly the azimuthal semicircle, the Ptolemaic rulers, the brass sextant with which to measure altitudes and the medium brass azimuthal quadrant, which instruments are depicted and described each in its place, viz. sub nos. 8, 9, 4, 3, the sequence in which they are enumerated here to be similarly understood in what follows, if necessary. P. [The letter P is not seen in the figure. This is the case for some of the following letters, too]. A globe upon which an instrument is placed when stellar distances are to be measured, in order that it may serve as support for it, so that the instrument resting upon it can be turned in every direction, as indicated above with the sextant sub no. 16. Corresponding to this there is a similar one on the western side. Q. An octagonal gallery on which the above-mentioned globe is placed. N. The smaller southern observatory containing the equatorial armillae, which are made completely of brass and denoted as no. 13. W. Stairs down to the laboratory and up to the observatory. R. The larger northern observatory, which is also full of a number of large instruments, viz. rulers or the larger parallatic instrument of brass, which also showed azimuths on a wall running round it, as explained sub no. 10 [cf. p. 49]. In the same tower also were the sextant measuring distances by one single observer [cf. p. 77], and the bipartite arc [cf. p. 69] and the instrument which at one time had been useful in the observations of the new star [cf. p. 81]. These three instruments have been described above sub nos. 17, 15, and 18. In the same place was also kept a parallatic instrument made of wood, which was formerly used by the great Copernicus and sent to me as a present from Ermeland, which I have mentioned in the place in question [cf. p. 45]. S. The smaller, northern observatory, which contains the other instrument with equatorial armillae depicted sub no. 12 [cf. p. 57]. T. Another globe similar to the one mentioned above, and serving as support of sextants, which are placed on top of it; corresponding to this one there is a similar one facing west. Further there is at the very top of the house, where some round windows are visible, eight bedrooms for the collaborators. ε. The uppermost octagonal chamber immediately below the spire of the house, from where there is a free view in all directions; round this there is a passage called the "gallery" on the top of the house itself. $\gamma\gamma$. Some octagonal constructions in which may be seen some carved figures representing the four seasons. $\beta\beta$. Seven chimneys ending in one in the south, and the same number in the north, so that all the chimneys of the whole house join in two different places. ν. A clock, the bell of which, ς, is hanging above. λ. A gilt Pegasus, which by means of a movable pointer found under the ceiling of the uppermost chamber states where the wind sits. In this place another pointer turning round the same axis shows the time. Such is the exterior of the house as seen from the east or from the west, and by a comparison between the south and the north side you will find the same appearance, so that everything corresponds mutually and is strictly symmetrically arranged, as required with architecture if the work is to be executed in a proper manner according to the rules of the art. As to the subterranean plan, which may be seen below denoted by dotted lines, it should be understood as follows: what is seen below the southern tower represents, as far as possible, the chemical laboratory. Here 1. denotes a round table placed in the middle of the room. On this the things may be placed which are to be treated. No. 2, as well as possible, represents furnaces of various kinds, placed here and there; there were sixteen of these, viz. three bath-heaters, a digesting furnace with ashes, four large *Athanors* and two small ones, two destillation furnaces with sand or ashes, one for a large bellows, connected with it by means of two pipes, another furnace placed apart, with lamps, two furnaces reflecting the heat, one directly, the other in a spiral, partly freely, partly in a closed chamber. Most of the furnaces were built of natural stones imported from Norway, the so-called Bergen stones, as they will stand even the hottest fire and may be worked up elaborately. But if everything in this laboratory were to be described, it could not be done briefly. What is delineated under the big house represents cellars, both pantries and larders underground. Here the doors through which it is possible to enter from the various directions, are denoted by no. 3, and the columns placed for support by no. 4. Under the northern tower at no. 5 is seen the built well, forty ells deep, mentioned under the ground-plan. Under no. 6 there are some built boxes in which food was kept. The rest partly appears from the picture, partly must be imagined.

ORTHOGRAPHIA STELLÆBURGI
EXTRA ARCEM URANIÆ SITI

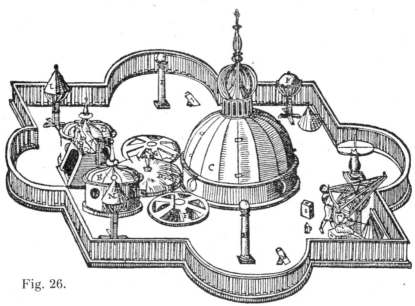

Fig. 26.

ICHNOGRAPHIA STELLÆBURGI

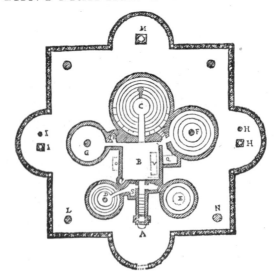

Fig. 27.

ORTHOGRAPHIA STELLÆBURGI EXTRA ARCEM URANIÆ SITI

DESIGN OF STJERNEBORG, LOCATED OUTSIDE URANIBORG

DESCRIPTION OF STJERNEBORG

Although the southern and northern towers of the main building of the castle with their additions on both sides might be sufficient for a suitable placing of a fair number of instruments, even if large, I did not, however, content myself with this. For as I for certain reasons had still more manufactured, which could not very well find room here, so that each of them could be used without getting in the way of another, I had later, about the year 1584, on a hill outside the castle situated about seventy small passus south of the wall, with no small difficulty and expenditure a subterranean observatory with various cellars built, erected from bottom to top of solid masonry.

My purpose was partly to have placed some of the most important instruments securely and firmly in order that they should not be exposed to the disturbing influence of the wind, and should be easier to use, partly to separate my collaborators when there were several with me at the same time, and have some of them make observations in the castle itself, others in these cellars, in order that they should not get in the way of each other or compare their observations before I wanted this. I called this observatory in Danish *Stiernburg*, nearly the same name as also used by the Germans, while in Latin it is called Stellæburgum. You see here a picture of its exterior together with its ground-plan, and they are explained in few words, as follows: A. A portal according to the Ionic order giving admission to the cellars of this observatory. On top of it there are three crowned lions elaborately sculptured, and on both sides there are some porphyry stones with suitable inscriptions included in vol. I of the Astronomical Letters, where this subterranean observatory is mentioned; but it would be too lengthy to repeat them here. Still, I shall quote the one found on the back because it is of a fairly general character. B. A round chequered ceiling above the heating

18*

installation, to which one is admitted from all directions from the cellars. C. A cellar for the placing of the largest equatorial armillae delineated sub no. 14 [cf. p. 65]. D. A cellar for the large quadrant, called the revolving one, which is described sub no. 6 [cf. p. 33]. E. A cellar for the zodiacal armillae explained sub no. 11 [cf. p. 53]. F. A cellar for the large steel quadrant inscribed in a square, denoted as no. 7 [cf. p. 37]. G. A cellar for the four-cubit sextant on its support and its revolving globe which is shown sub no. 16 [cf. p. 73]. So much for the cellars. But the above-mentioned inscription [Opera Omnia VI, p. 272 f.], which is written in gold letters on a porphyry stone on the southern back of the portal, runs as follows:

"Consecrated to the all-good, great God and Posterity. Tycho Brahe, Son of Otto, who realized that Astronomy, the oldest and most distinguished of all sciences, had indeed been studied for a long time and to a great extent, but still had not obtained sufficient firmness or had been purified of errors, in order to reform it and raise it to perfection, invented and with incredible labour, industry, and expenditure constructed various exact instruments suitable for all kinds of observations of the celestial bodies, and placed them partly in the neighbouring castle of Uraniborg, which was built for the same purpose, partly in these subterranean rooms for a more constant and useful application, and recommending, hallowing, and consecrating this very rare and costly treasure to you, you glorious Posterity, who will live for ever and ever, he, who has both begun and finished everything on this island, after erecting this monument, beseeches and adjures you that in honour of the eternal God, creator of the wonderful clockwork of the heavens, and for the propagation of the divine science and for the celebrity of the fatherland, you will constantly preserve it and not let it decay with old age or any other injury or be removed to any other place or in any way be molested, if for no other reason, at any rate out of reverence to the creator's eye, which watches over the universe.

Greetings to you who read this and act accordingly. Farewell!"

Outside the premises of this Stjerneborg some stone columns H.I. have been placed on each side, facing east and west; on these the Ptolemaic rulers may be placed, and if necessary, they can carry the small transportable armillae. K.L.N.O. are globes resting on their supports and now and then placed on the site mentioned in order that sextants may be placed on them when stars, in any place, are to be sighted. M. A round stone table intended, if required, for supporting the transportable quadrant and other minor instruments, that observations with these may be convenient. A clear-sighted and competent observer will easily discover the rest.

EXPLANATION OF THE GROUND-PLAN

A. A vestibule leading to a staircase giving admission to the observatory. B. A square heating installation. C. Cellar for the largest equatorial armillae. D. For the revolving quadrant. E. For the zodiacal armillae. F. For the large steel quadrant inscribed in a geometrical square, which is also made of steel. G. For the four-cubit sextant, which rests on its revolving globe. H.H. Some stone columns placed on the western side. I.I. Other stone columns facing east. K.L.N.T. Some globes placed outside to support the astronomical sextants. M. A round stone table. O. A bed on which I could sometimes be allowed to rest during the observations when accidentally there were clouds and we could not enjoy a constant clearness of the sky. Q. Another similar one, but more spacious, which might in the same way be used by my assistants. P. A stove. V. A table. S. Entrance to the subterranean passage which I had intended to have excavated under the wall and the garden, so that it might at some time lead into the castle and the chemical laboratory. For it has been commenced, but is not yet finished. The outer premises, including the gallery, on each side of their square facing the four points of the sky, measure 70 feet [cf. p. 9]; but the diameter of the semicircles found on the middle of the sides is 24 feet. In the two corners of this square area facing the south-east and the south-west there are some practically arranged cases, in which the large semicircular instruments with which stellar distances comprising more than one fourth of the circumference of the heavens are measured, and which are not depicted together with the other instruments, but only mentioned briefly after these, were carefully stored, as, besides, also some sextants and other transportable instruments, which need not be in constant use; and I had likewise decided later to place some in the north-east and the north-west corner. So much in brief about these subterranean buildings. If I should explain everything in detail, a very lengthy description would be required. But as to the poems which we have had inscribed in gold letters on both sides in the subterranean rooms, the same volume I of the letters offers information [Opera Omnia VI, p. 274 f.], and hence it will not be worth while repeating them in this place.

So much for the astronomical buildings. Although I had not intended in this place to mention the island in the busy thoroughfare of the Danish Sound, where we erected these buildings, I have thought that, as I have mentioned a highly situated and solitary place, and as this island has already previously been described by the illustrious GEORG BRAUN in the fourth volume of his *Theatrum urbium*, though indeed the presentation was not very true because of the negligence of the draughtsman, I therefore ought to describe it here with a somewhat greater accuracy.

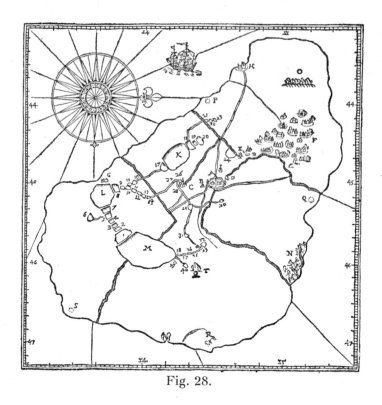

Fig. 28.

TOPOGRAPHIA INSULÆ VENUSIÆ VULGO HVENNA DICTÆ

TOPOGRAPHY OF THE ISLAND OF VENUSIA, POPULARLY CALLED HVEN

EXPLANATION OF THIS TOPOGRAPHY

This island is situated in the far-famed Sound in the famous kingdom of Denmark, that which divides Scania from Sealand, and the capital Copenhagen is situated at a distance of three miles south-west [the distance is 27 km], and Elsinore, with the Royal Custom House, is at a distance of two miles north north-west [this distance is 15 km]. These two towns are in Sealand. Helsingborg, which stands due north, is also two miles off [15 km], but Landskrona in the east is only one mile distant [9 km]. The latter two towns are in Scania. The island itself is very high, as if it were a mountain which you might ascend, but on top it is flat all over. Its circumference measures 8160 of the major passus. In the centre, where I have built the castle of Uraniborg, the polar altitude or, what amounts to the same, the latitude from the equator is 55°54¹/₂′, as measured several times by us with the greatest care. The longitude [cf. Opera Omnia V, p. 309] we have estimated at 36°45′, at which we have of course considered the difference between the meridians used by Ptolemy and Copernicus, and, as far as possible, the thorough calculations of the latter. Hence, on the square map on which the island is depicted, longitude and latitude are denoted in the way that each single degree is subdivided into seconds. What else is to be seen on the island is to be understood as follows. A. The castle of Uraniborg. B. Stjerneborg. C. The farm buildings. D. The workshop of the artisans, where they construct astronomical instruments, etc. E. A windmill. F. A village consisting of about forty farm-houses. G. A mill for the production of paper, and which may also grind corn and further prepare various kinds of hide, these three kinds of work being executed with one and the same very large wheel, all at the same time or each separately. H. The church. I. The place af assize of the peasants. K.L.M. Large fishponds, among which L, which belongs to the mill, is very deep and secured by means of an extremely heavy dam in order to be able to receive large quantities of water for the use of the mill. These fishponds and the rest, nearly sixty in all, which contain a great many different fishes, when necessary, out of consideration to the said mill, are without difficulty emptied of the greater part of their water. O. A marshy meadow, where some alder-trees are growing. T. Pastures, in part overgrown with scrubs. N. A small hazel scrub in the shadow of the north slope. P.Q.R.S. Ruins of four castles standing here in days of old. After King FREDERICK II, of glorious memory, as mentioned above, had left this island to me for life and certified this with a deed written on vellum, in order that I might there in suitable peace study Astronomy, I have spent a huge amount of work and much money in order to comply with the wishes of this excellent king and serve the honour of my native country: I have not only, as mentioned above, erected magnificent fixed buildings on the island, but also from everywhere collected as much water as possible, where there was none previously, in order that I might at once establish a paper-mill near the coast, which might supply paper for my printing-house, established in the same place, so that I should not have the trouble of providing it from Germany.

On all this I have spent more than a tun of gold [100 000 Rigsdaler]. For all that I could gather, either gifts from the King or from my own annual income, I spent on this object, to say nothing of the huge work and trouble I have undergone over there during twenty-one years. From this and several other facts every sensible person will easily conclude that I must have had very weighty reasons, particularly at the age of fifty and with a large family, to leave an island which to me had so great a value, and further my beloved native country and so many relatives and friends I had there. But which and how great reasons have moved me to do so, I prefer not to mention in this place. However, I want to excuse my Serene King, CHRISTIAN IV, my Most Gracious Lord, who has recently succeeded on the throne his father, King FREDERICK, of glorious memory, who laid the foundations of everything there and protected it. For I have no doubt that if he had in time and sufficiently been informed of all the facts of this affair, which cannot but redound to the credit of the realm, he would with his heroic spirit, his keen intelligence and noble mind, which is open to all free sciences, with which he is so excellently equipped, graciously and liberally have preserved these studies, which are so highly befitting to kings, within his realm, so that they might have been promoted there. But perhaps it was the will of fate that things developed like this in order that the redintegration of Astronomy might be known over an extensive territory and spread more widely over the world. Also this will be easily understood by everybody, how seriously and energetically the redintegration of Astronomy lie us at heart, since for the sake of it I have courageously wanted to bear so many efforts and so much expenditure, so many disturbances and so much adversity that I have not even hesitated to leave my native country and everything that was dearest to me.

So great was my desire to investigate the laws of the stars.

SUPPLEMENTUM DE SUBDIVISIONE ET DIOPTRIS INSTRUMENTORUM

ADDENDUM ON THE SUBDIVISIONS AND DIOPTERS OF THE INSTRUMENTS

Since I did not illustrate the transversal division and the diopters by drawings when speaking of the instruments, because such could not be provided quickly enough, I shall now add them here in order that this matter may be better understood. The method of subdivision by transversal points is apparent from this figure [Fig. 29], where every section of ten minutes by means of dotted lines has been divided into ten equal parts. In this way one obtains that the line of sight, when passing through one of these points during the observation,

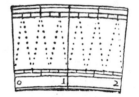

Fig. 29.

indicates the required minute of arc, or some fraction of it corresponding to the point from which it is deviating. I learnt this method of division in my youth in Leipzig, applied however to parallelograms formed by straight lines to which it is particularly well adapted. Later on I made it yield sufficient accuracy in applications to arcs on my instruments, as I stated in my book on the comet of 1577 at the bottom of p. 461 [Opera Omnia IV, p. 372]. Here I say as follows: "For although the proof of the correctness of this method applies especially to rectilinear parallelograms, it may yet be maintained with good reason for curved lines also without appreciable error, provided the length is so small that the deviation from a straight line is imperceptible". But in order now to add this proof, to a certain extent out of consideration to half studied persons who critisize things they do not properly understand, I give it here: In the accompanying figure [Fig. 30], let A be the centre of the instrument while A.O. is its radius. It is now assumed that O.I. is the part that is divided by transversal lines in the ratio 1 to 48, which is

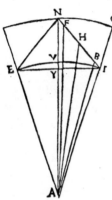

Fig. 30.

142

mostly used in my instruments [i. e. the width O.I. of the transversal division is ¹/₄₈ of the radius A.I. of the arc]. Supposing now that A.I. comprises 10000000000 parts corresponding to Rheticus' complete major table [corresponding to a ten-figure table], we find that O.I. comprises 208333333 of the same part, namely one forty-eighth of the radius. Now let the arc I.E. be 20', and I.V. 10'. The sinus of the latter angle, Y.I. is 29088779, while the sinus secundus, V.Y., is 42308 [this is $1 - \cos x$]. When the latter quantity is added to N.V., which is equal to O.I., it gives N.Y. equal to 208375641. Hence two sides in the triangle N.Y.I. which has a right angle at Y are known. From this it is found that the base [hypotenuse] I.N. is equal to 210396208, and that the angle N.I.Y. is equal to 82°3'10''47'''. Adding the angle Y.I.A. which is equal to 89°50', we obtain N.I.A. equal to 171°53'10''47'''. Now suppose the base N.I. of the rectangular triangle N.Y.I. to be divided into ten equal parts, so that one minute of arc, denoted by I.B., corresponds to 21039621. Further, in the obtuse-angled triangle B.I.A. two sides are given, namely I.B. and the radius I.A., together with the angle B.I.A. which is identical with the angle N.I.A., or 171° 53'10''47''', as we have found already. From this it is found that the angle I.A.B. is equal to 1'1''7''', while it ought to be 1'. Thus it is no more than 1''7''' greater than the true value, a deviation which is indeed imperceptible. Similarly, if F.I. is assumed to be equal to nine tenths [of I.N.], its length is equal to 189356587. Again we have a triangle F.I.A. in which two sides and the intervening angle are known, namely F.I. as just mentioned, the radius I.A., and the angle F.I.A. as before. From this we get the angle I.A.F. equal to 9'1''6''', while it ought to be exactly 9', so that the

Fig. 31.

last minute F.N. will be in error by 1''6'''. Finally, making the same experiment in the middle as we have just made at the extreme points, we find in the same way as before, first the angle I.A.H. equal to 5'3''6''', which is 3''6''' too great, next the angle N.A.H. equal to 4'56''55''', which is 3''5''' too small. [If N.A.H. is calculated as I.A.N. = 10' minus I.A.H., we find 4'56''4'''. All the numerical calculations are correct within one unit of the last figure]. Thus it is clear that the greatest difference to be added or subtracted in this process is a little over 3'', a quantity so small that a keen vision is in no way able to distinguish it in any instrument, and also negligible in itself. Those people who scoff at our method of division are therefore taking unnecessary trouble, as the method is sufficiently accurate. Indeed, in some of our instruments, especially in the larger ones with a longer radius, we usually perform this subdivision in sections of no more than five minutes. Consequently this small difference is even less appreciable, which was what we wanted to demonstrate in this way.

The arrangement of pinnules or diopters which we have found to be the most suitable is such that the lower pinnule, or that closest to the eye, has slits on all four sides, exactly corresponding to the upper pinnule in such a way that they are at the same distance from its four sides with regard to the line of sight and correspond to them. This is indicated in the accompanying figure [Fig. 31], as far as it was possible to do so on a plane surface. Here A.B.C.D. denote the pinnule that is held close to the eye of the observer, while E.F.G.H. is the other and more distant one which is located at the circumference of the instrument. Finally I denotes the alidade on to which these pinnules are fastened in a suitable way and at right angles to it. The pinnule F.G.H.E. must have exactly the same form as the other one, B.C.D.A. The small springs, however, which are mounted on the lower pinnule on three sides and which are perfectly straight on the sides facing the pinnule, can be pressed towards the pinnule or removed a little from it. In this way the slits can be made perfectly equal, and it is also possible to widen or narrow the slits during the procedure, should this prove necessary. This can be done by means of an ingenious special arrangement on the other, that is the inner side of the pinnule. By turning one single screw, that is by one single manipulation, it is possible to widen or narrow all the slits simultaneously without any trouble or waste of time. The fourth slit which is carved on that side of the pinnule by which it is fastened to the alidade, remains unchanged all the time. It is seen a little above B.A., and at the same distance from the plane of the alidade a second slit is seen in the upper pinnule at F.E. This innermost slit, however, can be made adjustable in width in the same way as the others by a minor addition to the construction.

The use of the pinnules is for measuring altitudes of the stars. The alidade I is raised or lowered until the star is seen through the slit D.A. and in the slit H.E. at the side of the other pinnule, while at the same moment just as much of the star is seen through the slit B.C. at the other side F.G. [The slightly awkward orientation of the alidade and the pinnules in Fig. 31 is evident from this]. In that case there can be no doubt that this star has been sighted centrally and accurately. If it is desired to find azimuths as well, one has to look through another slit C.D. towards the forward side G.H. and simultaneously through the slit G.H. [should be B.A.] towards the other side F.E.; in this way the stars are observed most quickly. In making solar observations however, circumstances are as follows. When the rays entering through a round hole in the upper pinnule in proportion to the amount of sunlight admitted by this hole in all directions fill a circle drawn on the inner side of the lower pinnule, then the required result is obtained. Further it should be noticed that in some instruments the pinnule farthest from the eye is of cylindrical form [cf. for instance p. 29]. The situation is the same as before, only it is now the shadow of the cylinder that has to be observed in the case of solar observations. Finally in the case of the armillae we make use of a round axis in order to make it possible to sight towards it from all sides. For both the cylinders and the round axes have the special advantage that they can be used not only by one but [simultaneously] by two observers. The rest will be clearer by a study of the figure, or rather through the actual use of such instruments.

This method of observation through slits that have the same mutual distance as those on the other pinnule I invented driven by necessity. For when using the method which is otherwise ordinarily employed, it is extremely difficult to see stars through holes, especially through the pinnule farthest from the eye unless it is sufficiently large; and in that case one may err by a considerable fraction of a degree, since it is impossible to know whether the sighting has been made completely centrally. In fact I am surprised that previous astronomers have not noticed it and somehow or other remedied this defect. A few years ago an excellent astronomer [Paul Wittich] came to visit me after a long journey in order to see my instruments. When he had become acquainted with this extremely convenient method of observing the stars through slits arranged in this way, he uttered a cry of joy and assured me that he had now come to know something that he had sighed for in vain for many years. He congratulated himself, finding that this alone made his journey to Denmark worth while. Later, when he came to Cassel, he applied this method as well as possible to the instruments of the Landgrave. He further introduced the method of division by transversal points, as appears from the passage in question in the first volume of the astronomical letters [Opera Omnia VI, p. 36] in the letters that were exchanged between Landgrave Wilhelm, of glorious memory, his astronomer, and myself. This discussion of the pinnules and the method of division must now suffice.